CW0408400

Reinventing the Wheel

Reinventing the Wheel

The Construction of **British Airways London Eye**
conceived and designed by Marks Barfield Architects

This book has been produced with the support and permission of:

British Airways
Marks Barfield Architects
The Tussaud's Group

Designed and edited by Ian Lambot.

Printed and bound in Italy by Conti Tipocolor s. r. l.

ISBN   1 873200 30 7

Contents

As a friend of David Marks and Julia Barfield, I had known about their dream to build the world's largest observation wheel in the very heart of London from its earliest stages. Indeed, I had worked out of their office for two years when I first returned from Hong Kong in the summer of 1995, and had watched on from the sidelines, so to speak, as the dream grew ever closer to reality — first with the granting of the planning approval in 1996 and then with the formation of the partnership with British Airways.

Even then, I had my doubts whether the project would ever see the light of day. But Julia and, in particular, David's persistence, determination and sheer bloody-mindedness should never be underestimated. For various reasons, explained in part below, I have not covered this early side of the story in detail in this book, but David and Julia's success in bringing the project to the point where it really would be built cannot be understated. While recognising the importance of British Airways and Bob Ayling's support throughout, it is a personal achievement every bit as great as the combined efforts of those involved since in bringing the project to its successful completion.

David and I had discussed the possibility of producing a book about the project's construction during these early days, but I can't say I had been that keen. In the 15 years since I published my first book under the Watermark imprint, all on architecture, engineering or design, I have produced several books on the construction of major building projects — most notably, the new headquarters for Hongkong Bank in Hong Kong (1983-86) and the Commerzbank building in Frankfurt (1995-97) — so it was not that I had no experience of such an undertaking, it was more that I was unsure whether such a book would have a broad appeal.

In all of these earlier books I had concentrated on explaining *what* had been built, rather than why. In part, this comes out of my own preference for the craftsmanship of the building process. Also, and perhaps more importantly, these were all buildings that had made significant advances

Foreword

in office planning and servicing; there were major lessons to be learnt that had a direct relevance for architects of all persuasions. Surely a similar book about the construction of the world's largest observation wheel would only be of interest to the designers of other observation wheels — hardly a thriving industry. I needed a theme with wider implications.

As noted above, I have never felt inclined to explore how prestigious buildings such as these come about. I have observed, often at very close hand, the political intrigue that inevitably swirls around projects of this scale and complexity but, other than to those directly involved, I have never been convinced that this is of any specific long-term relevance. There is, certainly, much to be learnt about the general human condition in such accounts — the inevitable in-fighting, the need for points to be scored and scores to be settled — but that is a different book entirely, and one that I am happy to leave to others.

Understandably, therefore, I was not entirely sure what to say when David rang me in December 1998 to say that, after many trials and tribulations, the project was at last going ahead. It was great news, but I was no closer to believing a book was viable. I was, however, sufficiently intrigued to attend a meeting a few days before Christmas to discuss the situation further. I was introduced to Tim Renwick and Fiona Hanan of Mace, and it was as they described how the project had developed and on what basis it was proceeding that the basic concept for this edition began to crystallise. As the meeting went on, I began to realise that what was of interest here was not the technology — although I must admit I underestimated quite how daring much of this would be at that stage — rather, it was the teamwork.

Listening to Tim explain the number of companies involved, their technical and geographical diversity, it became clear that success would only be possible if there was a true and complete understanding between all the parties involved — client, consultant and contractor alike. Everyone would have to play their part with a level of integrity, commitment and co-operation rarely seen on projects of this size. It was clearly going to be an extraordinary adventure and, quite frankly, I was hooked. I have not been disappointed.

As the book developed through 1999 and I got to know many of those directly involved, the correctness of that initial analysis has only been reinforced. In my experience, the level of dedication, passion and co-operation invested in this project by everyone concerned has been truly unique. And it is this, above all, that has made British Airways London Eye the success it is today.

It has been a privilege to be part of that process and to have spent time with many of those who have given so much to the project, at every level of the design and construction process, from lead designers and engineers to steel fabricators and systems operators. I can only hope that by focusing on and showing their efforts, I have captured in this book something of their passion and inventiveness, their generosity and good will.

Many, many people have helped me during the 18 months I have spent researching, photographing, interviewing and generally following the construction of this extraordinary structure. I cannot possibly name them all here, but to one and all I extend my sincere thanks. I can only hope that I will have the opportunity to express my gratitude properly in person over the coming months.

A few, however, deserve special mention and I would like to thank David Marks and Julia Barfield for asking me to be involved in the first place; Tim Renwick and Bob White of Mace, Paul Baxter of British Airways and Andrew Potter of The Tussaud's Group for their continued support as the book has developed; and Maarten Jongejan, Jacques Berenbak, Chiel Smits, Peter Koorevaar and Jan Stam of Hollandia, Johan van Kuilenburg of Mercon, Andrew Pugh of Heights of Abraham, Jean-Francois Savard and Philippe Desflammes of Sigma, John Roberts and Allan Mann of Babtie Allott & Lomax, Arie Lanser of Iv-Infra, Neil Thompson and Dave Smith of Mace, Steve Radcliffe of Tilbury Douglas, and Nic Bailey and Loren Butt for their time, their hospitality, their enthusiasm and their patience as I have struggled to make sense of just what it is they and their colleagues do. To those I have inadvertently forgotten, my apologies.

Ian Lambot
London, August 2000

THE BRITISH AIRWAYS LONDON EYE, conceived and designed by David Marks Julia Barfield Architects, was officially opened in March 2000, just over two months after the city of London had celebrated the birth of the new Millennium in a manner which had confirmed its status as one of the world's most important urban centres. For several months before that, however, the London Eye's huge circular form had already dominated the landscape. Its final move to a vertical position on the south bank of the Thames had been one of the capital's most breathtaking and memorable pieces of popular theatre. For a while it had hovered half in and half out of the water, unsure which way to move, providing an unlikely attraction for tourists and passers-by on a site which, though long neglected, was quickly becoming one of the most exciting areas of London.

The move from the twentieth to the twenty-first century was undoubtedly London's moment. Paris had had an impressive parade to mark the 200th anniversary of the Revolution of 1789, and other cities worldwide had their own millennial celebrations, but 31 December 1999, that special moment in time, belonged to London, the home of Big Ben and Greenwich Mean Time.

The London Eye played a key part in the transitional moment from one millennium to the next. It belongs, however, to the twenty-first century, and for Londoners in particular, but also for many others passing through England's capital city, it has become *the* symbol of the new Millennium. From one of its egg-shaped capsules a rider can take in the whole city and its outskirts from a single vantage point obtaining in the process an overview of the entire metropolis and a sense of place which was only previously possible from the air.

The London Eye is also a visual symbol of time itself, its slow steady movement marking the passage of time in the familiar analogue manner that is still embedded deep within our memories and which still means so much more to us than its digital equivalent. Not only is this dramatic new structure both an eye and a clock it is also, most obviously, a wheel — a circular metal structure with spokes and a hub which might once have belonged to a giant bicycle. Wheels have all sorts of associations for us, but perhaps none are as strong as those evoked by the ones which drove the machines of the industrial revolution and which helped to bring Britain into the modern age.

The wheel's creators, David Marks and Julia Barfield, were inspired by, among many other things, the entrepreneurial spirit, the technological virtuosity and the dynamic optimism and belief in the idea of progress that dominated the nineteenth and early twentieth centuries in the industrialised Western world and which made it possible for us to move forward, healthy and wealthy, into the twenty-first century.

Above all else, perhaps, the London Eye is a feat of construction which reminds us that it was the engineer, not the architect, who took us from the nineteenth to the twentieth century, and whose heroic presence at that time set the scene for today's celebrations of the modern world. Just over 100 years ago the likes of Isambard Kingdom Brunel, Robert Stephenson, Joseph Paxton and Gustave Eiffel were celebrated as heroes of their age, as the creators of structures which resisted gravity, conquered the forces of nature, gave men and women a new sense of their place in the world and, above all, acted as lasting symbols of the collective aspirations of whole nations. The monuments they created all became lasting icons of modernity, influencing many who have since sought to find new ways of representing the age of the machine in built form.

In particular the work of Brunel, which ranged from steamships to guns, from docks to railway stations and bridges (the best known of them being the Clifton Suspension Bridge at Bristol, designed 1829-31), showed the way forward. His mathematically-derived forms eschewed the decorative traditions and historical references so beloved of architects at that time, and quickly came to resonate with the excitement of the new age. Paxton's Crystal Palace — a large glass-and-cast iron greenhouse of a building constructed in London's Hyde Park to house the eclectic artefacts which made up the Great Exhibition of All Nations of 1851, the first international exhibition ever held — followed on in the same vein.

Rejecting the 'noble' styles of the past it opted for a new language of built form, which took its lead not from the masters of historic idiom but from the rationalism and utilitarian considerations of the engineer who sought to allow materials — especially new materials — to evolve a language of their own. Modern, democratic and machine-made, the building created by the ex-Chatsworth gardener captured the imagination of the British public in no time.

The new possibilities of mass production and prefabrication were such that the building was constructed in three months flat and contemporary newspapers described how large crowds of people, among them "high-born dames", came to marvel at this feat of new technology while it was being built. Although it was initially intended to be a temporary structure it was, in fact, reerected at Sydenham three years later and remained there until the 1920s when a fire finally destroyed it.

The London Eye stands in a direct line of descent from the excitement, optimism and energy of the Crystal Palace and from a number of other similar structures which, in their time, served to provide an unprecedented level of urban spectacle and to engender a link between constructed form and popular imagination. New York's Statue of Liberty and Paris's Eiffel Tower, among others, became the symbols not only of progress and modernity but also of democracy, power and imperial, national and civic pride. In them, the possibilities of new structural materials were exploited to the full to provide a set of lasting monuments which were characterised by their unprecedented size and their ability to dominate the urban landscapes around them.

Many of them were created for and then outlasted the very celebrations and exhibitions for which they had been conceived as intrinsic components. The Eiffel Tower, for instance, was built as an important architectural element within the ambitious International Exhibition held in Paris in 1889 and was used again as a key feature in the later event of 1900. Its great height — close to 1000 feet, the tallest structure ever erected at that time — ensured that it dominated the site on which it stood and gave it a tremendous sense of monumentality and authority which it retains to this day.

Previous page: **Gustave Eiffel's Tower in Paris — seen here during the World Exposition of 1900 with Walter Bassett's** *'Grand Roue'* **in the background — and Bassett's smaller wheel of 1897 for the Blackpool Winter Gardens.**

France had had its great proponent of the virtues of the modern engineered structure in Viollet-le-Duc who had written prolifically about the possibilities of iron in architecture, and in 1889 the architect/engineer team of Dutert and Contamin built, for the same exhibition as Eiffel's tower, the Halle des Machines which boasted an iron vault with a span of 385 feet and a height of 150 feet. Eiffel had experimented with some of the forms used in his tower in earlier designs for bridges, but nothing equalled the power of this dramatic punctuation mark in the sky. Not everyone was equally impressed by it, however. When asked why he was seen eating in the restaurant in this mammoth wrought iron structure the English craftsman, William Morris, who was so committed to the spirit of the mediaeval world, explained that it was the one place where he could not see it.

When the American engineer, George Washington Gale Ferris, proposed his giant wheel to the organisers of the 1893 Centennial Exhibition held in Chicago to commemorate 400 years of Christopher Columbus's discovery of the New World, he did not know that the format he was suggesting was to take on an iconic value which would still have a tremendous potency for us in the twenty-first century. Ferris's ambition was to make a wheel which was both bigger and better than any that had come before it, and which would provide visitors to the exhibition with both a dramatic form of entertainment and a means of getting a bird's eye of view of the whole event. Above all he wanted it to compete with the Eiffel Tower.

Trained as as a mechanical engineer, Ferris had run his own company which specialised in building bridges, railroads and tunnels out of steel before he ventured into wheel design and found a way of financing the venture himself. Like so many of the influential engineers of this time, he had to be an effective entrepreneur as well, and he put all his time and energy into getting his project off the ground and convincing the Exhibition organisers to let it go ahead.

Finally approved in December 1892, it turned for the first time on 17 June 1893 and proved to be an unprecedented success. Contemporary

Modern, democratic and machine-made, Joseph Paxton's Crystal Palace for the Great Exhibition of 1851 embodied the excitement of a new age.

newspaper articles recorded the drama of the event and the feelings of those who rode on it. A writer in the *Pittsburgh Commercial Gazette* described the first turn of the wheel as follows: "*Slowly, almost imperceptibly, it lifted the cars away from the earth, revolving from east to west. A fourth of the way up the wheel stopped. The passengers gasped in unison and looked at each other with smiles more or less sickly. They looked down and saw that they were hanging directly over the Austrian village. Suddenly they heard the regular throbbing of the engines again and felt much better.*"

Ferris's Great Wheel was 250 feet high and had 36 wooden cars attached to it, each of which held 60 people. Like the London Eye today it had little in common with the more modest fairground wheels, the sole purpose of which was to divert and entertain. For the vast numbers of people who went to the Columbian Exhibition it was the highlight of their visit. It towered above the rest of the structures and, because it moved as well as providing a landmark and viewing platform, it surpassed the Eiffel Tower in many American's eyes. Writing in *The Alleghenian* in 1893, an enthusiastic Robert Graves explained that "*the Eiffel Tower involved no new engineering principles, and when finished was a thing dead and lifeless. The wheel, on the other hand, has movement and grace, the indescribable charm possessed by a vast body in action.*"

Similar smaller wheels were to appear at the Californian Midwinter International Exposition of 1894 and the 1895 Cotton State Exposition in Atlanta, but the true successor to George Ferris was the English engineer, entrepreneur and retired naval lieutenant, Walter B. Basset, who was to construct four more Great Wheels in Europe between 1895 and 1900. The first of these — erected in Earl's Court to coincide with the 1895 Empire and India Exhibition — was based on a design patented in the UK by the American entrepreneur and inventor James Weir Graydon which, in fact, was little more than a copy of Ferris's design, increased in height to 270 feet but now with 40 cars carrying just 30 passengers each. For the subsequent wheels, however, a young engineer in Basset's employ who had worked on the Earl's Court wheel, H. Cecil Booth, was to make significant improvements, reducing the depth (and weight) of the rim and, as at the London Eye, holding the cars away from the main structure of the wheel in a separate frame.

The first of the new designs, a modest 200 feet in diameter, opened in Blackpool in August 1896, followed in 1898 by an all but exact copy in the Prater Park, Vienna. The last and — at 300 feet in diameter — the largest of the Bassett/Booth wheels, *La Grande Roue*, was erected a short distance from the Eiffel Tower as part of the Paris Exposition of 1900. The Great Wheel of Earl's Court was demolished in 1906, while those in Paris and Blackpool were eventually taken down in 1920 and 1928 respectively. The *Riesenrad* (literally, the 'Travelling Wheel') in Vienna, however, has had a far longer and more eventful life. Destroyed by fire-bombs in 1945, it was reconstructed a couple of years later and remains, to this day, one of the city's key landmarks.

Like Ferris's Great Wheel of 1893, the *Riesenrad* contained a level of drama, monumentality, popular appeal and national symbolism that

Walter Basset's Great Wheels for the 1895 Empire and Indian Exhibition at Earl's Court *(below)* — a close copy of George Ferris's original of 1893 — and his somewhat smaller version of 1897 for the Blackpool Winter Gardens *(opposite)* marked the passing of an era where heroic engineering had been the pre-eminent symbol of modernity.

Form over function. In a matter of decades engineering had given way to pure geometric shapes as the embodiment of modernity, as demonstrated by the Trylon and Perisphere, centrepiece of the New York World's Fair of 1939.

positioned it clearly within the tradition established by the Crystal Palace and the numerous other engineered structures that had acted as key dramatic components of the important national and international events of the second half of the nineteenth century. The power of the image of a wheel to carry the complex messages of the great nineteenth-century constructions proved short-lived, however, lasting only a matter of a few years. Until the construction of the London Eye a century later, where wheels were concerned, that intensity of meaning was lost and the concept of the Ferris wheel, as it came to be called, reverted to being one linked solely with the idea of popular entertainment and diversion.

Static monuments – whether permanent or temporary – once again asserted their power as the most effective markers of national and international achievements, commemorations, celebrations and power. From Manhattan's Empire State and Chrysler Buildings, or the Perisphere and Trylon at New York's World Fair of 1939, to the Sydney Opera House or,

more recently, Bilboa's Guggenheim Museum, it is bold architectural statements that have become synonymous with the concept of national authority. In recent years the architectural and engineering icons which have come to stand for late twentieth-century modernity and progress have begun to prioritise high culture over popular culture, seriousness over fun. In the process the sense of all-inclusiveness and democracy that had characterised the engineered constructions of the nineteenth century began to fade from view.

David Marks and Julia Barfield's design for British Airways London Eye has restored many of those latter meanings to the modern engineered structure. As well as asserting a new monumentality, a sense of grace and authority, a belief in the power of technology and in living in the present, in the tradition of the buildings constructed for the nineteenth-century international exhibitions, the London Eye also emphasises the importance of participation and pleasure. Its materials, its construction techniques and the multiple new technologies it has exploited herald the future in an unequivocal way. At the same time it provides an unprecedented level of access to the city of London and to its rich past. Like the Crystal Palace and the Eiffel Tower before it, it is both an object of delight and a serious monument, marking the cultural importance of London in the early twenty-first century.

The site on which the London Eye is located also has a special significance for the people of Britain. Although now only a living memory for those who have turned 50 years of age, the Festival of Britain, held on the south bank of the Thames in 1951, was an example of another event at which national prestige succeeded in coinciding with the popular imagination, and at which seriousness was combined with a sense of fun and celebration.

The Festival was conceived as a modern reinterpretation of the Great Exhibition held a century earlier, at a time when the British Empire was at the height of its power and Britain was an international force to be reckoned with. The Festival of 1951 was altogether different. Conceived by the post-War Labour Government as a popular national festival, its organisers were keen that, while the focus would be in London, the rest of the country would participate as well through local events and celebrations and travelling 'mini-shows'. The architecture of the Festival played a crucial symbolic role in the event and the South Bank site provided an opportunity for Britain's young architects — among them Hugh Casson, Basil Spence, Robert Goodden and Brian O'Rorke — trained in the ideas of the Modern Movement, and aware of parallel developments in Scandinavia, Italy, the USA and elsewhere, to 'go modern'.

Ralph Tubbs' Dome of Discovery and Powell and Moya's punctuation mark in the sky, the Skylon (two structures undoubtedly modelled on The Perisphere and Trylon which had made such a dramatic impact at New York's World Fair in 1939) were at the centre of the event sending out a clear message that Britain had finally found an architectural language with which to signal its arrival into the modern world. Today's London Eye is located right in front of the site on which, nearly half a century ago, the Dome of Discovery had welcomed visitors from all over England with exhibits celebrating *"British initiative in exploration and discovery"*. The London County Council's Festival Hall, the only remaining structure from the 1951 event, was separated from these key structures by the Hungerford Bridge, which divided the site in two.

The aims of the 1951 Festival, described as a *"tonic to the nation"*, were expressed as *"one united act of national reassessment, and one corporate reaffirmation of faith in the nation's future"*. Led by Gerald Barry, the planning team set out to find a means of *"demonstrating the contributions to civilisation made by British advances in Science, Technology and Industrial Design . . . exhibited in their practical and applied forms against a background representing the living, working world of today"*. The emphasis was upon the continuity of the past, the present and the future but, above all, on their significance for the people of Britain.

Over eight million people visited the Festival during the five months it was open. Its message was essentially a serious one, a moral boost to a war-worn nation keen to get back on to its feet, but its spirit was democratic and populist. The latter was enhanced by the presence of an overtly 'fun' element: the Pleasure Gardens located in Battersea Park. People amused themselves on the Big Dipper and the Tree Walk and stood in front of the Guinness Clock, created by Lewitt Him, waiting for it to leap into action. Today the London Eye combines all the messages of the Festival in a single structure. It provides both an education about the make-up of the city in which it stands, as well as a level of delight and pleasure for its visitors as they are swept up into the sky.

In 1951 the South Bank site was a run-down area of derelict wharves and warehouses measuring 27 acres, with only London County Council's County Hall, Waterloo Station and the, then, new Waterloo Bridge to give it any sense of identity. The Festival reclaimed four-and-a-half acres from the river and marked the beginning of the development of a site which has since seen the arrival of, among other structures, the Hayward Gallery and the National Theatre. Until the advent of the London Eye, however, the South Bank had never fully experienced the level of vitality and energy that it deserved and which the Festival of Britain had promised. Now, restaurants are opening almost daily and the area is buzzing with activity.

While, on one level, the London Eye pulls together a number of historical strands — which, from one perspective, can be seen to come at the end of a long tradition of monuments and events celebrating the modern age, new technologies and the advent of democracy — it is also a structure without a past, a new vision without influences other than contemporary ones. From another perspective, for example, it can be seen as a reworking of the revolving spaceship in Stanley Kubrick's film *2001*. It belongs to the present and, more importantly, to the future.

As a design the London Eye began its life as an entry for a competition for a structure to celebrate the Millennium which, thanks to David Marks and Julia Barfield's belief in the vision they had engendered — and their determination to hold on to it and see it through to realisation — moved from being a simple concept to a fully-fledged reality in half a

The power of architecture: at a stroke, Frank Gehry's design for the Guggenheim Museum has captured the public's imagination and transformed Bilbao into a World City.

decade. The story of that transformation is a complex one, characterised at different moments — as are all significant achievements — by feelings of hope, optimism, anxiety, disappointment, exhilaration and, ultimately, a tremendous sense of pride. In the end, the simplicity of the basic idea of a wheel from which people could see the city of London in a way that they had never seen it before remained uppermost, giving its visionary designers something to hold on to during the many moments when the challenges of resolving so many details seemed almost overwhelming.

The London Eye is much more than a mere icon. It is an experience which changes your life. Once you have taken a ride in it and seen London from the unique vantage point it offers, your sense of the city is transformed in a way that hours spent pouring over a map could never achieve. Not only is the layout of the city unexpected and strange — the fact that the river is moving from south to north at this point is the first disorientating realisation — the landmarks you thought you knew are replaced by others you have never quite noticed before. Every ride is different, transformed by the time of the day, the weather conditions, the position of the sun, the changes of light, the night-time illumination of buildings or just the small things you happen to notice in the half-hour it takes to make the full circuit.

At the same time, given the nature of our media-oriented society and the enormous impact of its image, the London Eye cannot avoid becoming an important mass icon as well as a personal experience. Such is its iconic power that, in the short time in which it has existed, its visual presence on television and in the newspapers has been difficult to ignore. Politicians of all persuasions have used it to show that they are both 'of the people' and 'of the moment', proving the depoliticised nature of the wheel but showing also that it can lend its meanings to whichever political party wishes to exploit it. Its multiple meanings, combined with its strong silhouette, clean lines and photogenic appearance, have made it the logical backdrop for countless publicity shots for key cultural figures and television personalities, as well as a location for a royal birthday outing.

The London Eye's iconic status is a marker both of the strength of its design and of its enormous popular appeal. Its simple, dynamic form has entered into the public consciousness at a speed that could not have been fully anticipated. Its accessibility is immediate, both as a reproduced image and as a reality. Its dramatic form, viewed from different angles, can be seen from many points in central London and further afield. It appears suddenly and unexpectedly on the skyline in the gaps between buildings but, although imposing, it does not conceal anything, as its delicate skeletal structure acts as a transparent tracery through which everything else remains visible.

The challenge now for the London Eye is to maintain its impact. Many of the city's other dramatic symbols of modernity have not survived the test of time, but British Airways London Eye may be different. Already, it seems set to enjoy a quite different fate. As its creators David Marks and Julia Barfield have said from the beginning *"its sole purpose is to delight"*, and by delighting first and educating second there is every chance that it will maintain its appeal for many years to come.

For a country still recovering from the ravages of war, the Dome of Discovery *(opposite and below)*, together with the Skylon at the 1951 Festival of Britain, symbolised the beginning of a new era of peace and prosperity. As Britain enters the twenty-first century, it is entirely appropriate that the British Airways London Eye, conceived and designed by David Marks and Julia Barfield, should now stand on the same site.

A big wheel for London

eter Popham welcomes a bit of vulgarity on the river.

ppointed to a second
of the Royal Fine
is dead against it.
Society wants to
k Art Centre's
the way it is:
ir teeth over
ng. All that's
of Wales to
que – an
rom the
nglet

But the grounds are in any case very
strong. As the architect Piers Gough
has pointed out, there has always been
a dichotomy between the dignities of the
Thames's North Bank – Parliament, Big
Ben, Somerset House and so on – and
the frivolity of the South Bank –
art and theatre, its
and Oxo Tower,
trasy was

In recent tin
become bl

18

"There is an innate desire in all men to view the earth and its cities and plains from 'exceeding high places', since even the least imaginative can feel the pleasure of beholding some broad landscape spread out like a bright coloured carpet at their feet, and of looking down upon the world as though they scanned it with an eagle's eye. For just as the intellect experiences a special delight in being able to comprehend all the minute particulars of a subject under an associate whole, and to perceive the previous confusion of the diverse details assume the form and order of a perspicuous unity; so does the eye love to see the country or the town, which it normally knows only as a series of disjointed parts (as abstract fields, hills, rivers, parks, streets, gardens or churches), become all combined, like the coloured fragments of the kaleidoscope, into one harmonious and varied scene. With great cities, however, the desire to perceive the dense multitude of houses at one single glance, instead of by some thousand different views, and to observe the intricate network of the many thoroughfares brought into the compass of one large web, as it were, is a feeling strong on everyone – the wisest as well as the most frivolous – upon all, indeed, from the philosopher down to the idler about town."

Henry Mayhew
After an ascent in a hot-air balloon, 1882.

The earliest sketches of what is now known as British Airways London Eye first saw the light of day in December 1993, prepared by the architectural husband and wife team of David Marks and Julia Barfield in response to an 'ideas' competition for a monument to celebrate the turning of the millennium. Their inspiration was to provide a sweeping view of London from a new landmark at the very heart of the city. Their initial research led to a remarkable series of drawings of the city *(left)* — made by W. L. Wyllie and H. W. Brewer in the 1880s in response to a new craze for panoramas made from hot-air balloons — which captured the spirit of their proposal exactly. Unaware, at this stage, of the parallels with George Ferris's and Walter Bassett's work on Great Wheels at the end of the nineteenth century, their initial design — developed in association with Jane Wernick of Ove Arup & Partners — for a visually light but stately wheel was prepared from first principles.

"It all started on 23 October 1993, when I came across a piece by Richard Rogers in that week's Sunday Times announcing an ideas competition for a landmark to celebrate the millennium. The submission date was 4 January 1994. We didn't do much about it initially, other than some vague discussions that it had to be different: not another staid monument, but something uplifting; something that would put a smile on people's faces; something they could participate in. The trouble was we had no real idea what that might be, until the thought struck me, out of the blue really, that it had to be a view of London, a really complete view that would take in the whole city."

David Marks
Director, Marks Barfield Architects

Drawn as part of the competition entry, these early sketches demonstrate clearly how little the original concept has changed over time. Indeed, a brief verbal description could easily be referring to the completed British Airways London Eye: the site is unchanged and the size is more or less the same; the capsules are held well away from the rim to allow unobstructed views in every direction; and the rim itself is supported on just one side and cantilevered out over the river. The only major difference was that in the search for greater visual lightness, these early designs explored the possibility of a single supporting 'arm' between the hub and the rim. In reality, this proved too heavy if sufficient 'stiffness' in the overall structure was to be maintained and later designs reverted to the use of more efficient — and hence far lighter — tensile spoke cables.

"I just knew it had to be Jubilee Gardens. If it was about London, it had to involve the river; and if it was about appreciating London from a new perspective, where better than from the heart of the city. Once you bring the two together, you soon realise there is no real alternative."

Julia Barfield
Director, Marks Barfield Architects

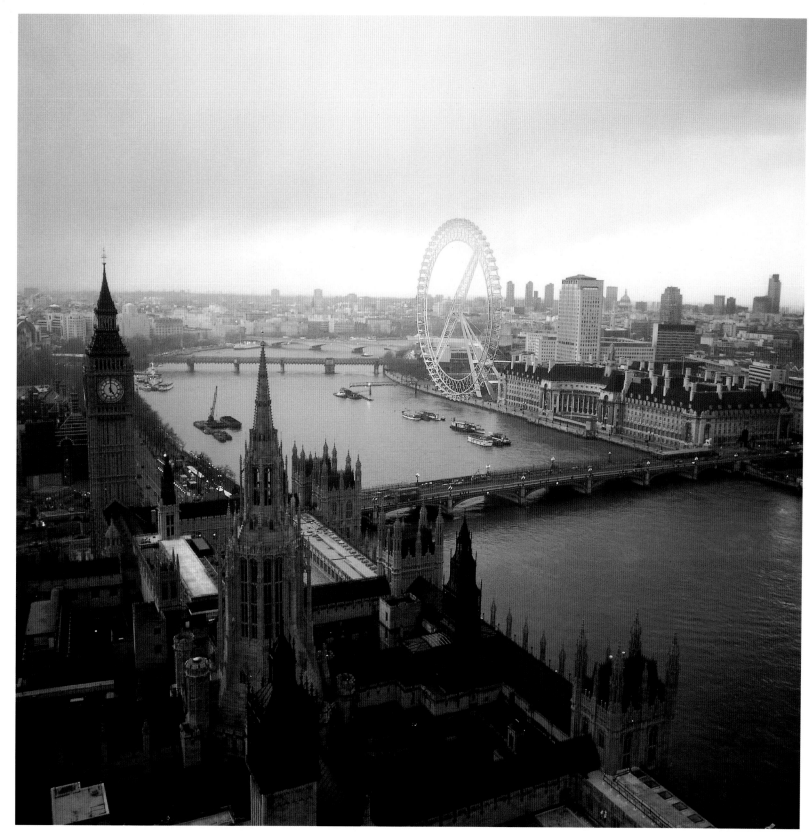

Every architectural competition demands at least one arresting image. With no time for a model, a computer-generated photo-montage seemed the perfect solution and, by good fortune, David and Julia were able to arrange, for photographer friend Nick Wood, access to the perfect vantage point: the top of Victoria Tower at the Houses of Parliament.

"That was it, then; (Marks) and Barfield would offer to build the biggest sightseeing wheel in the world. Not a Ferris wheel — pooh to that, with its fairground flash — and certainly not a white-knuckle ride. This would be an observation wheel that travelled slowly, majestically. It didn't at all faze Marks and Barfield that the first Ferris wheels had been built well over 100 years ago. Indeed, what they wanted to capture was exactly the spirit of the 1851 Great Exhibition in the Crystal Palace — such belle époque spiffiness! As to where to site their moving experience, Barfield clinched it. 'Obvious! Only one place for it,' she said. 'Jubilee Gardens on the South Bank, where the Skylon and the Dome of Discovery had stood during the 1951 Festival of Britain.' An iconic landmark for an iconic site."

Peter Martin
The Sunday Times Magazine, 14 November 1999

Nothing of substance was to come of the competition, but David and Julia's proposal captured many people's imaginations. With the encouragement of friends and relatives, they decided to press on and on 10 February 1994, together with David's father Mel, they set up The Millennium Wheel Company to develop and promote the concept. Aware of the controversy a new landmark on the skyline of London might provoke, a series of realistic photo-montages was prepared, showing how the wheel would look from various locations around the city, including *(above)* a night view from Waterloo Bridge and *(right)* a view from the Embankment.

"We realised at the outset that consultation would be the key, and we spent a lot of time in those first few months arranging meetings – with planners from the London boroughs, with local MPs, with the landlords of County Hall, with the Port of London Authority, with the Arts Council and the South Bank Centre, and with all sorts of local interest groups. It was an interesting exercise. A lot of people grasped what we were trying to do immediately and were incredibly supportive, but others were not so sure. There was a *definite element of elitism in many of the comments – that it would lower the tone, would attract hordes of ice-cream vans, that sort of thing – which is why we started doing more computer-montages, to prove that the wheel was above that, was something special. Then the Evening Standard picked it up and began a 'Back the Wheel' campaign which was incredibly helpful."*

David Marks
Director, Marks Barfield Architects

By the end of 1994, David Marks and Julia Barfield had demonstrated that the building of the wheel was entirely feasible. It was clear, however, that significant investment was required if the project was to proceed further. Following a meeting shortly before Christmas with Bob Ayling, then British Airways Chief Executive, and a series of top-level discussions with the airline's finance and marketing team to evaluate the project, British Airways came on board as a partner in July 1995. Immediately, Jane Wernick and her team at Ove Arup & Partners were appointed to carry out detailed design studies necessary to prepare the project for full planning approval.

0.75m rim 60 guys

4m rim (triangular) 30 guys 3pt formation

10m rim (radial) 12 guys 4pt formation

Early studies on the road to Ove Arup & Partners' final design *(far right)* included a sequence of drawings comparing the number of cables with the size of the rim *(right)* as well as sketches exploring how the wheel might be supported from as few points as possible *(above)*.

"I first became involved in the project in December 1993, when David and Julia asked if I would be willing to help with their competition entry. This was essentially in my spare time at that stage, with help from my colleague Sophie le Bourva. Then, it went quiet for most of '94 and I didn't really get involved again until the beginning of 1995. They were talking to British Airways by then and needed some additional advice on costs and so on. But the real design work only moved forward later in the year, when British Airways committed to underwrite the design development costs – around September I think. Then, everything started to happen very quickly. A whole series of studies were implemented: traffic movements, visitor predictions, buildabilty, power sources, capsule design, environmental controls, interference to radio transmission. The list was endless and it was my role to co-ordinate all the information and feed it back into the design. We also undertook a full structural design review, which led to the use of spoke cables to support the rim rather than the single stiff arm of the competition entry. This, in turn, led to a very thorough series of studies looking at how the arrangement of cables and rim geometry affected issues such as metal fatigue and buckling of the rim. David and Julia were very concerned that the wheel should be visually as light as possible, so we made a series of drawings showing how the number of cables affected the size of the rim. We settled on 20 pairs of cables, with each pair connecting one point on the rim's inner chord to either end of the hub."

Jane Wernick
Project Director, Ove Arup & Partners

"I first came on board in 1997, around July, when the project suddenly moved up a notch as it became increasingly clear it was really going to happen. London is British Airway's home base and the company brings more passengers, more travellers and overseas visitors into the UK than any other airline, so the project did have a business relevance, but it was clearly outside the norm. We consider ourselves experts on the technology of aeroplanes, for example, but the engineering here was entirely different – a lot of new technologies beyond our experience. This was also a tourist attraction, but while we might know a good deal about helping people to their destination, we don't normally become involved in what they do once they are there. At this stage, we still didn't have a complete financial package either, so it was all quite scary in many ways – tremendously exciting but also very fraught – trying to balance technical and commercial feasibilities and keep the project moving forward. But at the end of the day, you always knew you were working on something special, a project that was bound to make a big impact, and we all thought that it was just too exciting to be part of something so dramatic and let it pass by."

Paul Baxter
Project Director, British Airways London Eye

As part of the planning and consultation process, this beautiful model of London was prepared to prove that the wheel would not impinge unduly on the views from the city's other major landmarks. It served its purpose well and, on 22 October 1996, full planning consent was granted.

The design was now well advanced and a number of companies were approached to offer advice. The German company FAG prepared an initial design for the main bearings, while the Poma Group in France — specialists in the design fabrication of cable cars and ski-lifts — were commissioned to build a mock-up of the capsule. Babtie Allott & Lomax were appointed independent checking engineers, and the Dutch steel fabricator, Hollandia, advised on erection methods. By November 1997, the project was ready to go out to tender.

In November 1997 the project was put out to tender as a turn-key operation, with one company or consortium being asked to take full responsibility for the wheel's overall design and construction — a decision that was to mark the end of Ove Arup & Partners involvement in the project. The Japanese company Mitsubishi was selected in January 1998 and two months later Mace, one of the UK's leading project management firms, came on board to act as project manager. Two months later, in March 1998, The Tussaud's Group — who operate many of the UK's leading attractions and who had been considering the project for some time — also agreed to join the team, becoming a full partner in October.

As spring turned to summer, it became increasingly clear that Mitsubishi were struggling as the true complexity of the project became apparent. In June, the company proposed a compromise design, reducing the overall height of the wheel by 10 per cent to 135 metres and reducing the number of capsules from 60 to 32. With considerable reluctance, the proposal was accepted — a decision that was to form the basis of the final 'as-built' design shown here — but it was to no avail and in August 1998, by mutual consent, Mitsubishi withdrew from the project.

"When it became clear that Mitsubishi, for whatever reason, weren't going to be able to deliver the wheel everyone expected, it was a truly terrible moment. It seemed that was the end of it, but at the same time there was a real reluctance to let the project die. We had become too emotionally involved; we couldn't just walk away; we all knew we had to find a way. There seemed to be three alternatives: move ahead with a scheme none of us believed in; give up (and if we knew then just how difficult the project was going to be, we may well have advised that); or go back to Hollandia and Poma and see whether they felt able to take the job on, at short notice and nine months late, but still deliver on time. It seems mad that we even suggested it now, but somehow it set us all a challenge: if we went in this direction, and if Hollandia and Poma agreed, we were all accepting that we were going to do what-ever it took to complete the project. There would be no going back and no time for doubts. Hindsight is a wonderful thing but I think it's fair to say that everyone saying 'Yes, I'm in,' was one of the true defining moments of the project."

Tim Renwick
Project Director, Mace Limited

"In early December 1997 I approached Marks Barfield Architects to ask if they realised there was a requirement under the Health & Safety Executive regulations to appoint an independent checking engineer for any project deemed to be a 'passenger carrying device'. Basically, this covers everything from roller-coasters to monorails, and has been put in place because most of these structures fall outside the scope of the standard building regulations. At its simplest, the independent checking engineer is responsible for anything to do with passenger safety, from assessing the initial engineering design, including methods and calculations, right through to physically testing the operating and safety systems. Everything has to be checked, tested and approved before a member of the public is admitted. We knew that very few architects or engineers would be familiar with these issues but, having worked on many major ride projects, we felt that Babtie Allott & Lomax had a particular expertise to offer.

Following meetings with David and Julia, Jane Wernick and, of course, British Airways, we were appointed as the overall independent engineer for the project. We were soon faced with a dilemma: while it was essential we maintain our independent role, it was clear that this project was so complex it was in no one's interest to stand back and wait until the project was completed before passing judgment. Instead, we made the decision from the outset to become an active

A computer-generated perspective *(left)* by Marks Barfield Architects, showing the final design prior to construction complete with all the major elements:

1 steel rim
2 hub and spindle
3 A-frame legs
4 spoke cables
5 main back-stay cables
6 capsule
7 boarding platform
8 restraint tower
9 pier
10 collision protection boom
11 compression base
12 tension base

In early September 1998, Hollandia formally agreed to join the project as contractor with responsibility for the engineering and construction of the wheel structure and its drive mechanism. Mace took on the role of construction manager and the Poma Group was appointed to design and build the capsules. The design team at Marks Barfield Architects *(below)* geared up for a new role overseeing the development of the final design — including work on the boarding platform, restraint towers, capsules and landscaping, the latter in association with landscape architect Edward Hutchison. The Sumitomo Bank and Westdeutsche Landesbank Girozentrale also came on board at this time, as part of a revised financial structure. In December, Tilbury Douglas Construction Ltd were awarded the contract for site and marine works. Following a formal groundbreaking ceremony on 28 January 1999 *(below left and bottom)*, British Airways London Eye was under way.

member of the team, giving approval to the different design, fabrication and commissioning stages as they occurred This came into its own when Hollandia and Poma came on board, as we were able to brief them impartially on all the design work that had been carried out previously."

Dr John Roberts
Project Director, Babtie Allott & Lomax

33

Despite the very tight schedule, Hollandia's first decision when taking on the project was to instigate a complete design review, to be carried out by the company's own engineers with support from a local consultant firm they had worked with before, Iv–Infra. It was a time of meetings, whether between Professor Jacques Berenbak, Chiel Smits and David Marks *(below)*, Johan van Kuilenburg and Maarten Jongejan *(below right)*, or the many others not shown here who were soon swept up into the project's embrace. By late October, a clear direction had been determined which would allow the structural design to move forward. Detailed analysis would take many more months, but it was now possible to prepare a complete set of preliminary shop drawings — including a detailed analysis of the rim structure *(right)* — which allowed the first components to be put out to tender. Fabrication of certain components began in a matter of weeks.

TOP VIEW OUTE

6000

Spoke Co

SIDE VIEW

"Maarten (Jongejan) rang me out of the blue one afternoon from Rotterdam Airport. He was in a meeting and he needed to know if we could take on around 60,000 hours of work at short notice as he didn't have the capacity. He would not say what the project was; the only clue he gave me was that it was something round. I asked him if it was in London — but I was thinking of the Millennium Dome. It turned out we had the space in our schedule and I could say yes, in principle. We met a few days later and he told me what was going on with the wheel, the work they had done before and his impressions of the design. I can't say I was too confident; there seemed to be a lot of difficulties. It was an exciting challenge, but I don't think either of us was really sure if we would succeed. We agreed to hold a review then if we would go on."

Johan van Kuilenburg
Managing Director, Mercon Steel Structures BV

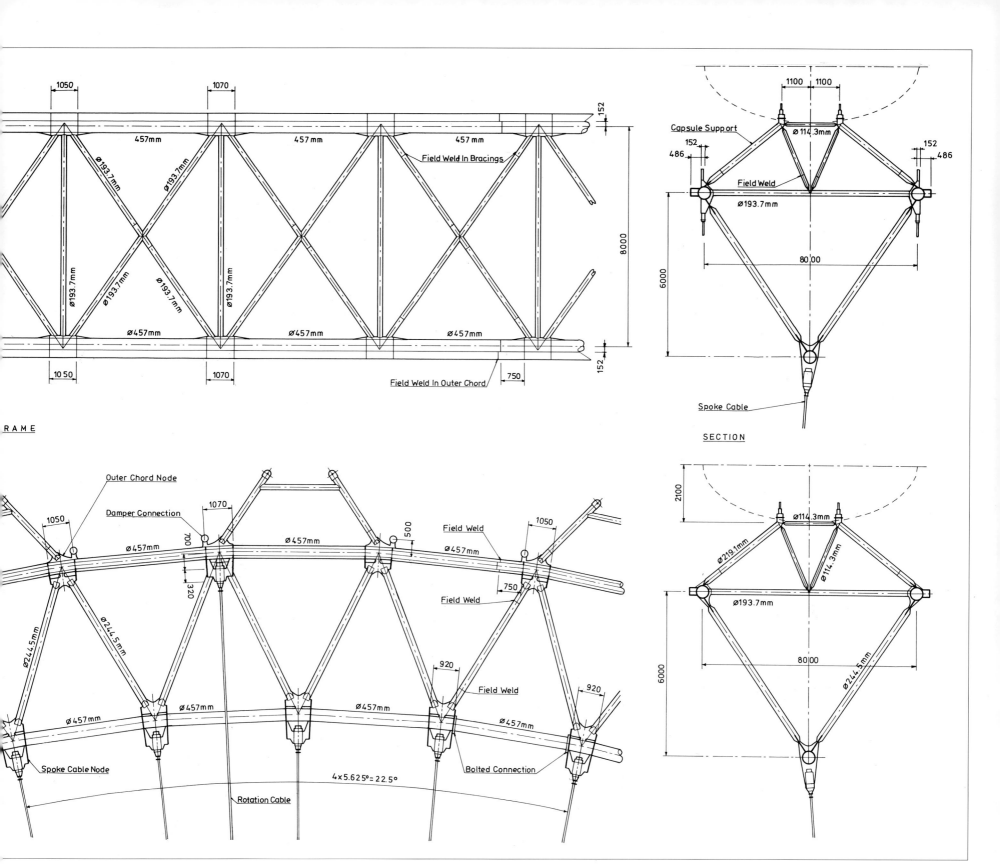

FRAME

SECTION

1050 1070 152 457mm 457mm 457mm Field Weld In Bracings Ø193.7mm Ø193.7mm Ø193.7mm Ø193.7mm Ø193.7mm Ø193.7mm 8000 Ø457mm Ø457mm Ø457mm 152 10 50 1070 750 Field Weld In Outer Chord

Capsule Support 1100 1100 Ø114.3mm 152 486 Field Weld 152 486 Ø193.7mm 6000 80 00 Spoke Cable

Outer Chord Node Damper Connection 1070 1050 500 Field Weld 1050 700 Ø457mm Ø457mm Ø457mm Field Weld Ø244.5mm 320 750 Ø244.5mm Field Weld Ø457mm Ø457mm Ø457mm 920 Field Weld 920 Ø457mm Spoke Cable Node Bolted Connection Rotation Cable 4 x 5.625° = 22.5°

2100 Ø114.3mm Ø219.1mm Ø114.3mm Ø193.7mm 6000 80 00 Ø244.5mm

"That first meeting at Rotterdam Airport came as a big surprise. As a contractor, you are hardly ever asked to work in a way that offers total control. The pull to say yes was very strong. Jobs of this profile and with these sorts of challenges do not come along very often, but this was not a decision you could make emotionally. I knew I had to be realistic, to tread carefully. I discussed the situation with my colleagues at Hollandia and made a few calls to people whose help

we would need to make sure they had time available, then said I was interested but would need two weeks to analyse the drawings. Very quickly, it became clear there were a number of areas which needed to be looked at in more detail and we had to ask for more time. At this stage, we really could not be sure. We felt we were working at the limits of what was possible and any moment we might find something we could not control, so we began to pull in all the people we could think of to help: all of our own people,

of course; specialist companies like Iv-Infra, Mercon, Skoda, Croese and FAG; and experts we knew with experience in cable design, damping systems, tube connections and so on — areas where we did not have too much experience. Always, we tried to find the best people in their fields. Only then did we have the confidence to move forward."

Maarten Jongejan
Managing Director, Hollandia BV

By mid-February, when the photographs shown here were taken, Hollandia had completed much of the detailed design work for the different elements that make up the main structure of the wheel, and production had begun in earnest in factories all over Europe. Many hundreds of dedicated craftsmen soon found themselves caught up in the excitement of working on this unique project. Shown here are just a few of the steelworkers who worked on the project at Mercon Steel Structures, their main efforts at this stage focussed on the fabrication of the complex tubular connections, or nodes, for the rim sections.

Cast-steel nodes were considered but the time required to complete all the necessary calculations before casting could begin would have added weeks to the programme. A delay at this stage could not be risked and it was decided, instead, to proceed on the basis of welded plate connections. Though not as smooth as castings, discussions between the architects and the engineers ensured a high visual quality was maintained.

"My main impression of those first few months is that we had meetings rather than correspondence. I set up what were meant to be short progress meetings every Friday, but every week they turned into a major design review with long technical discussions. It was one of the few times when we were all together and we all understood that a problem for one of us was a problem for everyone. It was better to solve it there and then. Everything happened very fast – decisions were made and we moved on. If we were unsure about anything we would bring in an expert the following week and work with their advice. Always, there was someone looking over our shoulder, not to take responsibility but to ask questions, make us think again, think carefully. We never looked back. It was a case of trying to identify what information could be released even though everything else was still in progress; that's how we were able to order the steel tube before we had completed the engineering drawings, and later to start the cutting schedules before we knew all the welding procedures. It was incredibly demanding, but also very exciting. And it was very successful – we had to change very little when the calculations finally came through and all the steel we ordered was used."

Chiel Smits
Project Manager, Hollandia BV / Mercon Steel Structures BV

February 1999 and the master jig that will support the different components of the rim structure during final assembly takes shape in Mercon's main assembly hall *(left)*.

The fabrication of the rim sections began with the assembly of the smallest repetitive elements, the nodes. Hollandia had determined that direct tube to tube connections would not be strong enough to sustain the forces acting through these complex components and, working with TNO Bouw (the National Research Institute for Building Materials and Structures), had developed slotted connections using transverse and intermediate plates. These dramatically increase the contact area for each weld and improve the transfer of forces through the connection as a whole. Carefully considered welding sequences and purpose-designed jigs ensured the tight dimensional tolerances required were strictly maintained. As the nodes were completed, they were set out on ever larger jigs and joined by steel tubes to form the rim's inner chord *(above)* and then the outer frame *(following pages)* before the two were brought together in the main assembly hall.

The fabrication of the different pieces that make up the completed rim section was carefully broken down into discrete elements, steadily increasing in size and complexity but always in such a manner that overall dimensions and alignments could be adjusted and corrected at each stage to ensure the exacting tolerances were always met. The outer chords took shape in one part of the factory *(bottom left)* while the capsule support frames *(right)* were assembled in another. To ensure the pin-joint connections for the capsules were correctly aligned, Hollandia had prepared two matching jigs, one supplied to Mercon *(below)* and one to the capsule manufacturer, Sigma.

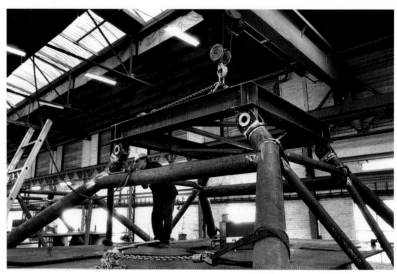

"We are specialists in welded and tubular-steel structures, so the fabrication of the individual parts of the rim was not that unusual. The tolerances were very small, so we had to look very carefully at all the welding sequences — first, how the different parts were made and then how all these parts were assembled — to make sure everything stayed as straight as possible. You must take care because every time steel is heated and cools it shrinks a little. But this is our usual work. Our real problem was that this was an aerial structure.

With a building you start from a solid foundation and correct as you go, but with this there was no real reference point. Instead, we built a number of three-dimensional templates (or jigs) in which we could position the pieces very accurately, but even then we had to be careful not to leave any stresses in the structure, which might cause the section to twist later."

Johan van Kuilenburg
Managing Director, Mercon Steel Structures BV

Working from a master set of shop drawings supplied by Iv-Infra, the in-house fabrication drawings, welding and cutting schedules and other ancillary design work – including the design of the jigs – was carried out in the Mercon drawing office by the company's own engineers.

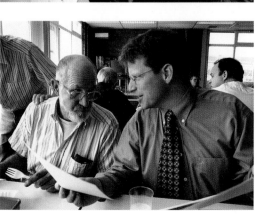

"There was always so little time. It was a bit like an express train: slow to start but difficult to stop once it was moving. But you also knew you were working on something special, something the whole world would know about. Even my neighbours, once they found out what I was working on, would stop me to ask how things were going – which never happens usually."

Alex Rietveld
Project Engineer, Mercon Steel Structures BV

As the individual elements that make up the rim sections grew in size, ever greater care was necessary to ensure fabrication was carried out to the levels of accuracy required. Working up from smaller to larger sections allowed minor discrepancies to be corrected at each stage, but only within very fixed limits which became ever harder to achieve as the pieces grew in complexity. And the tolerances were very tight indeed. The 9-metre overall width of the outer frame for example, shown here during final assembly, could be exceeded by no more than 5mm. Of greater concern was the straightness of the whole frame. It was essential that movements out of plane in the completed rim, both horizontally and vertically, were kept to the absolute minimum to ensure a constant alignment with the boarding platform when the wheel was completed. Guiding systems were to be installed in the restraint towers to position the wheel correctly as it turned, but the greater the pressure required to keep the rim in place, the greater the fatigue loadings produced — both within the rim itself and in the restraint towers.

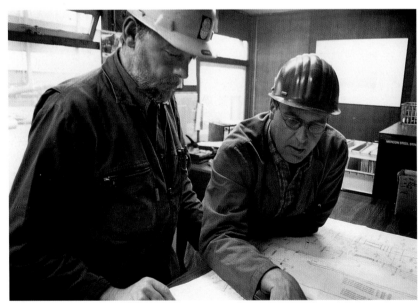

Work procedures were carefully planned with the welding teams and monitored throughout by the production managers — including Gerard Nederveen (above) — to ensure the highest quality was maintained.

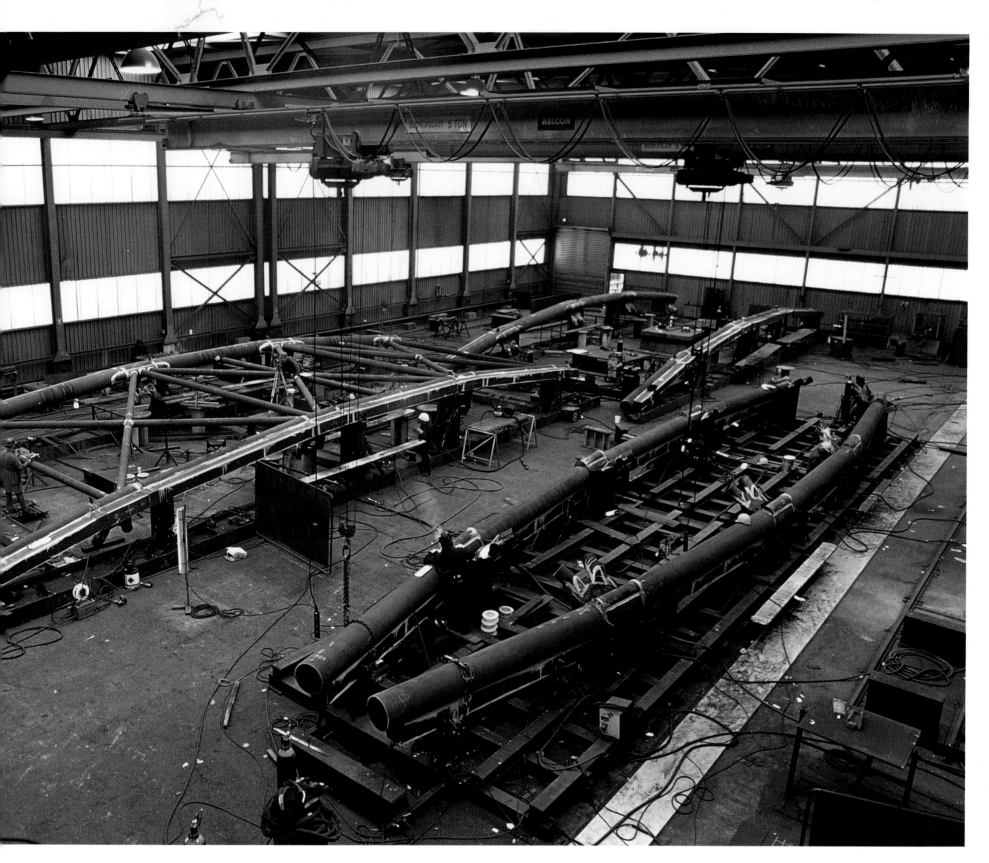

"It was our job to decide how each piece was made. The yard manager, the two other production managers and myself would normally sit down with Alex Rietveld to sort out what other shop drawings and cutting profiles might be needed. With most welds you can predict, say, up to 70 per cent how much it will shrink, but never exactly – that depends on the welder and the quality of the steel. So we monitor the first part and make corrections, then check the second piece and so on until you get every piece as accurate as possible. Every welder has his own technique, so we tried to keep the same welders on the same sections. We started with the nodes, but it was the same idea for the bigger sections, except here you could cut the connecting tubes to fit the first time and only pre-cut the rest of the tubes later when you had everything worked out."

Gerard Nederveen
Production Manager, Mercon Steel Structures BV

The assembly of the rim's inner chords and outer frames commenced at the beginning of March, and before the month was out the first of these were being brought together in the main assembly hall *(main spread)*. Here, sections of the rim's triangular truss could be completed, three at a time, on a master jig to ensure that each section aligned perfectly with its neighbour. As each section was finished it was lifted, turned and placed into a separate jig, to allow its capsule support frames to be added to the 'top' of the outer frame. At this stage, the rim was fabricated in equal one-sixteenth sections. Measuring some nine metres wide and just over six metres deep (8.5 metres including the capsule support frame), each of these 24-metre long sections weighed 36 tonnes when complete and incorporated over 450 separate welded connections.

The final stage of the assembly of the rim sections, the fitting of the diagonal bracing between inner chord and outer frame had to be carried out with complete accuracy. Great care was taken to position the different elements within the main jig precisely before welding began, and the welding procedures themselves were closely monitored. The slightest misjudgment might have induced twisting in the rim, which would have been very difficult to remove. Working 24 hours a day in shifts, Mercon's most experienced welders completed the work without error and on schedule.

"It was very important that we minimised the building tolerances at every stage. This was relatively easy when the sections were in the factory, but would be much more difficult outside. We decided the best solution was to make a three-dimensional survey of each section as soon as it was completed. Each piece was supported at three points to ensure it was stable and then measured very thoroughly, so we knew its exact size and shape. This was done for the one-sixteenth sections before they were painted, which allowed us to set them out precisely before they were welded together to form the one-quarter sections. Then we did the same with the quarters sections before they were shipped to London. Our initial design strategy had assumed the rim would be out of plane by plus or minus 150mm, but the final result now the wheel is finished does not exceed even half of that."

Nardo Hoogendijk
Design Engineer, Hollandia BV

April 1999 and the first batch of completed one-sixteenth rim sections *(right)* are lined up outside Mercon's main assembly hall, ready for transporting by barge to Hollandia for shot-blasting, painting and final assembly. The sections' triangular form made the sections inherently stable, but great care was still required when lifting them out of the jig *(below)* and setting them down to avoid any risk of twisting or damage. The unsupported sections of outer chord at one end of each rim section — which would later form the connection to its neighbour — were particularly vulnerable. And while a certain degree of rusting is inevitable when working with bare steel, it was clearly beneficial to move the sections as promptly as possible so that the appropriate corrosion protection could be applied.

"From the outset, we were aware that we were responsible for 800 people, responsible primarily, of course, for their safety — which concerned the structural integrity of the wheel — but responsible also for their comfort, which has much more to do with the dynamic behaviour of the wheel under wind loadings. Then there was the problem of the lack of time — we had to decide our priorities very carefully, decide which calculations

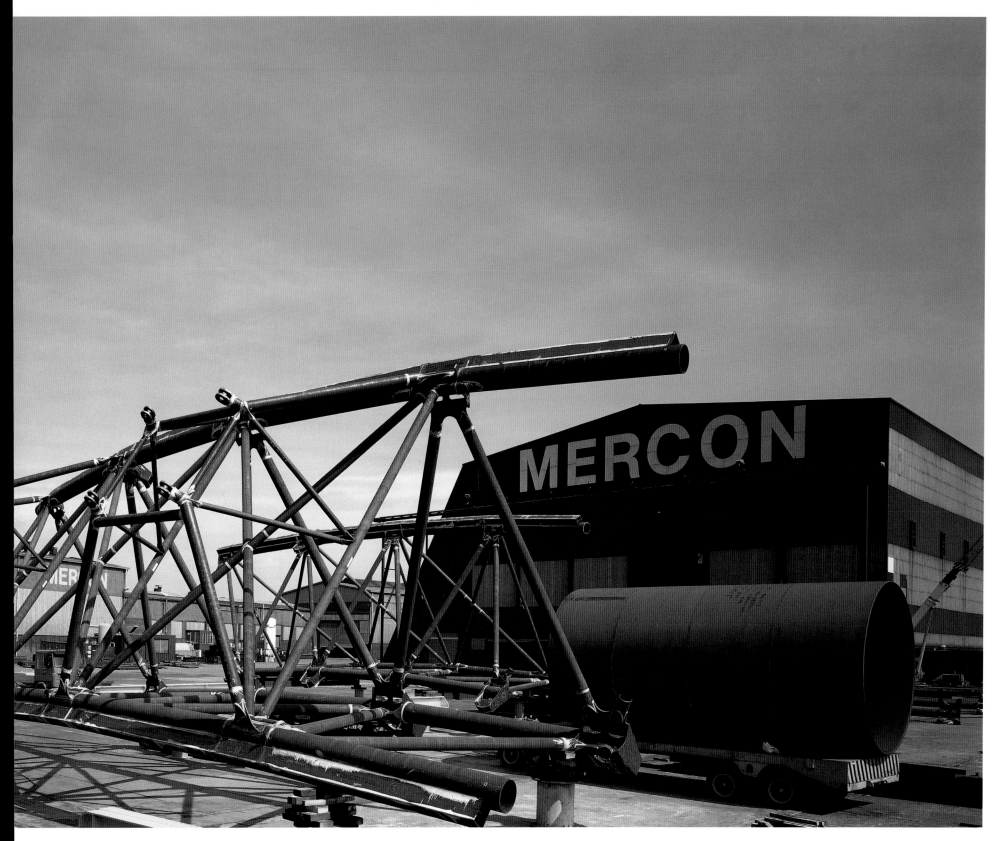

were essential now and which could come later. We brought in a number of experts from TNO Bouw to do some risk analysis, to check our technical reference points and to advise on areas where we lacked experience. Professor Bert Snijder from Holland Railconsult was also asked to check all our drawings and working methods, and to point out if we had missed anything, raising questions and

making recommendations. We analysed every part of the structure, asking what would happen if this occurred or that, identifying which parts were redundant and which were not, and making the necessary allowances. With the most critical parts, we took a higher safety level than that mentioned in the codes. The effect of fatigue was a major concern. Analysing how the nodes would react as the forces on them changed every time the wheel made a rotation was very time-consuming.

Fortunately, a recognised authority on tube connections, Professor Jaap Wardenier, was able to advise us on the detailing and calibration of the tailor-made welded rim nodes."

Professor Jacques Berenbak
Senior Design Engineer, Hollandia BV
and Professor, Delft Technical University

"The one major advantage we had was that we had the capability in-house to control every part of the process, from design to fabrication to erection. A decision on one part of the process invariably had an effect on the other, but everyone we needed was here and they already knew each other well, which allowed decisions to be made very quickly. That was a great help."

Maarten Jongejan
Managing Director, Hollandia BV

54

On their arrival at Hollandia on the outskirts of Rotterdam, just a few hours by barge from the Mercon works at Gorinchem, the rim sections were lifted on to the quayside by floating crane *(opposite)* and transferred as quickly as possible, first into Hollandia's purpose-built shot-blasting facility and then, when all the preparations had been completed, into the adjacent paint shop *(above and right)*.

"Iv-Infra was involved from the very first day, helping with the analysis of the original proposal, then working closely with Professor Berenbak at Hollandia to develop their new design. Our main responsibility was to carry out the structural calculations and prepare all the drawings for the many steel components — the rim, hub, spindle, legs, restraint towers and boarding platform. Everything was interrelated, so we had to keep a good overview, but each element also had its own governing factors. The cables had to be pre-tensioned to avoid them going slack in certain wind conditions, but the greater the tension the greater the risk of buckling in the rim. There was also the problem of fatigue in the cables, the nodes and in the capsule support frames, caused by the turning of the wheel. Most of these were non-linear calculations which required the use of finite element analysis. In fact, the calculations were so complex and so critical that Hollandia asked the Municipal Engineering Office of the City of Rotterdam to check the calculations using a different computer program. There was also the problem of analysing movement and accelerations in the wheel due to varying wind loadings. Many of these calculations had to be repeated over time, with thousands of calculations for many points on the wheel. We had to consider every situation and the number of calculations was unique."

Arie Lanser
Project Manager, Iv-Infra

The decision to fabricate the rim initially in independent one-sixteenth sections was made at the outset. It was a logical division of the rim as a whole, based as it was on 64 equally-spaced spoke cable connections, while the sections themselves were the optimum size to be comfortably accomodated inside Hollandia's shot-blasting and paint halls. Each hall is fitted with its own air-conditioning system to ensure low humidity levels are maintained at all times, thereby offering the very best conditions in which to carry out the cleaning, repairing and testing of the sections — all in the shot-blasting hall — as well as the final painting. Three coats of paint were applied: a zinc primer, followed by two coats of marine-quality white gloss epoxy to all parts of the rim except the drive rails along the sides of the outer frame, these being finished with a 'high-grip' aluminium magnesium coating.

In early May, just three short months after fabrication of the first node connections had begun, the first one-sixteenth rim section was towed out of the Hollandia paint shop resplendent in its final coat of white paint and moved to the main assembly area next to the dock. There, it was lifted by floating crane (opposite) and carefully postioned on temporary supports, ready to be welded to its neighbours (below) to form the one-quarter rim sections that would be shipped to London. In a little over four weeks, the first of the completed quarter rim sections would start its journey to London, where a small team from Hollandia were already in residence preparing the temporary site supports and river platforms for its arrival.

"Hollandia has a long experience of building movable steel structures: swing bridges, flood barriers, lock gates and so on, many different projects. And this has taught us how important it is to think about how they will be put together from the beginning. You look for the best design, but always you must consider the technical implications. You must try to think ahead and work out what the problems will be in three or four months time, during the different assembly phases, during the transport of the different pieces or when they are lifted into place on site. Every stage should be as simple as possible, but at the same time, because there will be very little time to change things or add pieces later, it is important to complete as much as possible before the move to site."

Peter Koorevaar
Technical Director, Hollandia BV

The final assembly of the one-quarter sections was carried out by both Hollandia and Mercon, each company completing two sections on their respective outdoor assembly areas. Using the accurate surveys undertaken earlier, the completed one-sixteenth sections were first laid out very precisely to minimise any misalignments. The final connecting pieces — including a complete section of the inner chord, two diagonal braces and two short sections of the outer chords — could then be accurately cut to length and welded or, in the case of the inner chord, bolted into place. The final shot-blasting, testing and painting was then completed under full-height shrouding positioned where required.

Measuring some 88 metres long in their completed form, the one-quarter rim sections were larger than the barges that would be used to transport them to London by some margin. Careful preparations were required therefore, in particular with the setting out of the main support cradles, to ensure the rim was securely held in place and the whole barge was well balanced.

"Babtie Allott & Lomax have been involved in many major projects over the years, from large naval facilities and power stations to work on The Royal Opera House. We have also been involved with other 'rides', roller coasters and so on, both as checking engineers and as designers in our own right — and, set against these other projects, I can honestly say that this is one of the most complicated structural engineering projects we have ever undertaken. There were all the problems of fatigue analysis, of course, then the dynamic behaviour of the wheel and its response under different wind conditions. The use of heavy steel castings introduced a number of problems you don't usually come across, as did the whole issue of buckling in the rim due to the tension in the spoke cables. A great deal of analysis was required, but the real problem was understanding what sort of analysis and how to apply it. It can be quite difficult to get your mind round what is actually happening with a lot of these problems — when buckling occurs for example — but you need a fairly clear understanding if you want to know what to do about it. Not surprisingly, the project has made huge demands, both emotionally and time-wise, but it has also been tremendously exhilarating. I doubt whether many of us would have missed it for the world."

Allan Mann
Technical Director, Babtie Allott & Lomax

61

The end of May and the first of the completed one-quarter rim sections is being lifted on to the barge that will transport it across the North Sea and up the River Thames. The decision to move the rim in quarter sections had been determined by a number of factors, including what size cranes might be available on site and the difficulties that might be encountered when transporting the finished sections up-river. Detailed research had been undertaken, for example, to ensure the loaded barges would fit under all the bridges downstream from the site. At the same time, it was preferable to move the rim in as few sections as possible, as this minimised the need for time-consuming welding on site, as well as limiting the number of temporary platforms required in the river. To reduce the amount of on-site work to an absolute minimum, the rim sections were shipped as complete as possible, with their emergency access ladders, temporary work platforms and electrical connection rails already in place.

The main elements of the hub and spindle were, for the most part, manufactured in cast steel. Measuring 24.6 metres long and with an overall diameter of 2.15 metres at its widest point, the central spindle was far too large to cast as a single piece. Instead, it was produced in eight smaller sections, seven of which were cast while one, the straight-forward cylindrical element between the bearings, was formed in rolled steel tube — this being more economical for the thickness of steel (80mm) required at that point. Two further castings, in the form of great rings some 4.6 metres in diameter and 900mm thick, form the main structural elements of the hub, a simple rolled steel tube forming the spacer that holds them apart. As with all the structural components, the design was carried out by Hollandia's in-house design department, with extra structural analysis being undertaken by Arie Lanser and his team at Iv-Infra *(below)*. The casting work itself was carried out by Skoda Steel, its foundry at Plzen in the Czech Republic being one of the few capable of handling the large and very precise castings required.

"The forces acting within the hub are so complex that they always had to be castings, but we did consider fabricating the spindle to begin with, at a larger diameter, as a means of saving time. Our main concern, however, was the bearings — we knew there would be a long lead-time for these as there would be a lot of design work to complete before fabrication could begin. We decided to talk to FAG in Germany — we had worked with them before — and it turned out they had already done a design for Ove Arup & Partners based on a cast-steel spindle. This needed revising somewhat, but was basically ready to go into production. Because of the time, their design became the fix for the overall diameter of the spindle and that, in turn, meant it had to be a casting. Technically, we knew this was a good solution and, fortunately it turned out Skoda were able to start work right away."

Professor Jacques Berenbak
Senior Design Engineer, Hollandia BV

"Everything had to happen very quickly and there was no time for a formal tender process. Instead, we had informal discussions with the foundries we knew could do the work — to find out who was available, what they might charge, that sort of thing — and this identified Skoda very quickly. They had worked with us before, so we knew they could produce the quality we wanted and, because they knew us, they were willing to take a flexible attitude, to start the work before we had completed the design. We knew by then that if we wanted to keep to the schedule we had to cast the main pieces before Christmas so that we could use the three week holiday for the cooling down period. This left just 12 weeks for us to complete all the design work and for Skoda to make the patterns and moulds. It was very tight."

Peter Koorevaar
Technical Director, Hollandia BV

The casting process begins with the fabrication of a full-size wooden pattern of the piece to be made, at the size it will be cast — usually a good deal larger than its final form as only the metal at the centre of the casting retains the high quality required. Shown here, during the preliminary stages, are the patterns for the two massive cast-steel 'feet' that support the main A-frame legs, but the same process was used for all the cast spindle sections, as well as the two cast components that make up the hub. To allow the work to proceed as quickly as possible, the detailed sizes of the spindle sections were released in stages, the external shape being fixed a week or so before the internal profile had been finalised.

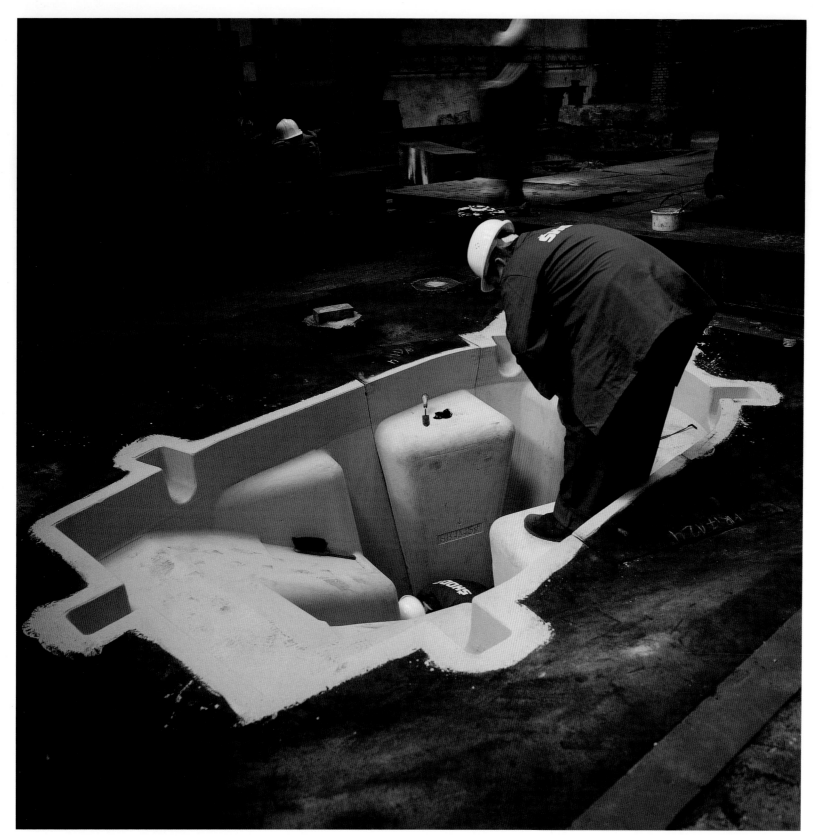

The moulds are formed in a fine, densely packed black sand, mixed with a special resin to help it hold its shape. This is built up around the patterns in deep pits set into the casting hall's floor, with care being taken to ensure that the pattern, which may be built in sections, can be removed as the mould takes shape. Separate supply tubes set into the surrounding sand channel the molten steel to the right parts of the mould during the pour.

"The most important thing about this project was that we had to learn new ways of working with other people. The work itself was not that unusual: this was not the biggest casting we have ever made, and it was not the most challenging in the technological sense. What was special was that we had to work closely with the designers – receiving the information in a raw state, working from very simple drawings, making changes. I am not sure every foundry would have been able to work in such a way. We need a high degree of trust between ourselves and Hollandia, a good co-operation, a good understanding. The information came in stages, which required more communication and more discussion, and not everyone here was happy with this – the late changes and so on. Everything was very fast. Everything was different – the work, the agreements, the financial side. We had never worked like this and we had to find many new procedures. Fortunately, we had worked with Hollandia before and we have a good relationship with them, and that allowed us to work this way. It was not always easy for us, but it was a very good experience."

Václav Sístek
Deputy Managing Director, Skoda Trading

69

Although the casting of the main hub and spindle sections had been completed in January, the decision to assemble the wheel horizontally resulted in two further castings being required, both of which were poured on 6 April 1999. These were the two massive 'feet' that support the main A-frame legs. Weighing around 23 tonnes each in their final form (nearer 50 tonnes at the time of casting), these were the most difficult pieces to cast, as the combination of a very heavy central mass with relatively thin outer flanges made it more difficult to control the cooling of the different parts at a steady rate. The pouring of the molten steel — from the furnace into the crucible *(below)* and from the crucible into the mould *(right)* — was as dramatic as ever, particularly as at Skoda much of this work is still carried out by hand.

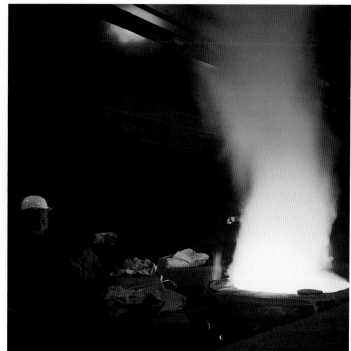

To ensure consistent strength throughout the thickness of the final casting, the speed with which the molten metal cools in the mould is as important a part of the process as the quality of the raw steel. Only a slow and even cooling will ensure the metallurgical properties of the steel are consistent from the centre to the edge. For the largest sections, this cooling might take up to four weeks, and is carefully monitored at all times by numerous sensors and heating elements built into the mould to ensure the temperature falls at the correct rate.

One of the hub castings, shown here being cleaned of unwanted material after the first of three heat treatments it will receive before final machining. These eliminate undue stresses in the metal and take place after each major stage in the machining process. At this stage, the casting weighed around 50 tonnes and was still considerably oversized — even if already much reduced by the removal of a riser weighing a further 30 tonnes. Though cast as a single element, each hub has two distinct layers: a large diameter circular flange, on to which are secured the 32 spoke cables, and, slightly above, a smaller faceted flange for the eight rotation cables. The machining itself was carried out in stages, beginning with the removal of the spigots along the sides of the casting — indicating where the molten steel entered the mould — and an initial rough machining. Three further machinings would be required before completion, by which time each hub section would measure 4.64 metres in diameter and weigh no more than 33.5 tonnes.

For ease of handling and to allow use of the most accurate turning machines, most of the spindle was cast in sections between two and three metres high. Shown opposite is one of the tapered sections that will form the back of the spindle during its second machining. Both the inside and outside of the section were machined, the entire operation being controlled by computer to ensure the correct wall thicknesses and angle of taper were achieved. With greater continuous strength required around the main pin-joint connection, only the central section was cast at an increased height. This is shown here after its first machining *(below)*, complete with an extra bulge around the bearing point to ensure the best quality, and later *(right)*, during the second machining of the main pin-joint.

"I would not say any of the casting was a problem. We worked with Hollandia to decide how the sections were broken down, working out where we needed continuous strength and where welds were possible. We also had to consider the final machining, what was the best size for our turning machines. The most difficult piece was the centre part of the spindle — where there are the connections for the legs — but this was mainly because of its size. It weighed more than 180 tonnes when cast and was over seven metres high, which required a very big mould and careful control of where the metal entered, to make sure it was filled evenly and completely. The design of the mould comes partly from experience, but we also have our own computer programmes, developed here, which indicate which areas are critical so we can make the right allowances. We had to add a lot of extra material to the thickness of the main cylinder itself — with even more over the critical areas — and also to the height. This part is called the 'riser' and it is needed to squeeze all the flaws out from the centre of the casting. It was cut off as soon as the casting came out of the mould. When it was finished, the casting was five metres high and weighed around 70 tonnes, so you can see there is a big difference."

Václav Bocker
Sales Department, Skoda Steel

"The most demanding aspect of the project was the lack of time. This was particularly true of the spindle. We really needed more time with that – at Hollandia and at Skoda. We had to work fast, but we had to make sure everything was made in a good way the first time. There was no time to make a piece again if we found a fault in the first casting, and this created a lot of pressure. Fortunately, I had worked with Skoda before – on the storm surge barrier project – so I knew they had the technical expertise. I had a good relationship, too, with most of the people there which was a big help. Even so, I was visiting Plzen nearly every week in the first few months. But it all went very well. In fact, the only real mistake was mine. We decided to cast a small plaque listing the main companies involved in the design and construction of the project on one of the feet, but I forgot to include Mace. Of course, they picked it up during a visit to Skoda when the feet were being machined – it was very embarrassing. Fortunately, we were able to weld the name on afterwards and now you cannot tell."

Adry Zondervan
Quality Assurance Manager, Hollandia BV

Appearances can be deceptive. In spite of a machine hall that seems to have changed little in decades — and working practices long unseen in European factories — the machine operators at Skoda Steel, some of whom are shown here, continue to produce castings of unsurpassed accuracy and quality on equipment, particularly in the Nuclear Machine hall, as up-to-date as anything found in foundries elsewhere.

The most important of the hub and spindle sections were finished on specialist turning machines capable of working down to the 15-micron (0.015mm) tolerances required where the bearings are seated.

"*Making the moulds before the design was finished worked quite well. We were only caught out once, when an extra access point was added to one of the tapered sections late in the design stage. As there was no time to wait, it was cast before Iv could complete the engineering. They found a few 'hot-spots' for stress, but we were able to weld some ribs along each side of the opening later.*"

Peter Koorevaar
Technical Director, Hollandia BV

The final machining of the spindle and the two main parts of the hub was carried out in the Nuclear Machine hall, a separate section of the Skoda works usually dedicated to the production of complex components for power stations, nuclear reactors and the aerospace industries. Here, the different parts of the spindle were welded together to form three intermediate sections, two around 10 metres in length, this being the largest size that could readily be transported by road to Hollandia. The largest of these was the central section *(above)*, shown here having its temporary external fixings being removed after welding. Meanwhile, in another part of the workshop *(opposite)*, one of the hub sections is shown during final machining.

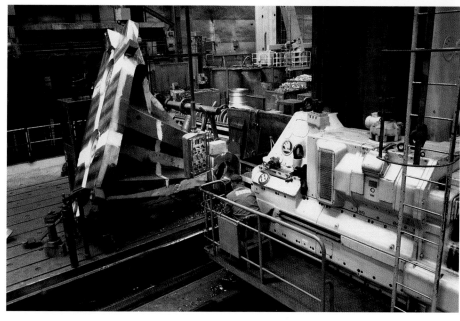

"The welding of the cast steel sections and the final machining was carried out here in the Nuclear Machinery hall. This is where we keep the most accurate machinery and the very best testing equipment. Our main concern was to meet the very high quality required, so each operation was prepared as carefully as possible. We started with the welding. The pieces were brought together and held in place with external fixings. The inside section of the weld was completed first and then tested thoroughly before being independently assessed and approved. Then the external fixings were removed and the outside of the weld was completed. It is a standard operation which we have carried out with steel up to 500mm thick, so the 200mm or so thicknesses we had here were not a problem. Once the welding had been tested again and approved, the castings underwent a final heat treatment for stress relief and annealing, and then they were ready for the final machining. We had tolerances of 15 microns for the most critical sections and around 2mm elsewhere, but the machinery here is made for this sort of work. Our only real concern was the centre section, with the heavy pin-joint connection on the one side. Even with the machine turning slowly, the extra weight would have caused some distortion, so we added a counterweight on the opposite side and tested this carefully to ensure a good balance."

Frantisek Picek
Manufacturing Manager, Skoda Steel

The massive A-frame legs that support the entire wheel were fabricated in tubular rolled steel by SIF, a Dutch company specialising in the making of pipelines and pressure vessels for the off-shore and petrochemical industries. Measuring some 58 metres in length and 3 metres in diameter at their centre, tapering down at each end, the two legs were delivered to Hollandia in their raw unpainted state, each leg in two sections. At 48 metres, the longer sections *(below)* were the maximum size that could be readily accommodated in the paint hall, while the shorter sections *(right)*, the last 10 metres of the lower ends, were easier to handle during their final fit-out. This process began with the welding of the external fixing brackets — into which are anchored the back-stay cables that hold the wheel vertical.

The brackets for the back-stay cables *(left)*, were welded into place on the outside of the A-frame legs, while fit-out work proceeded within *(below)*.

Hollandia had considered fabricating the legs in thinner steel, lined internally with stiffening ribs, but quickly realised the time this would take was not cost effective. Static calculations showed that producing the legs in 30mm-thick rolled steel would provide the strength required without stiffeners, but fearing problems with vibrations the decision was made to specify a final wall thickness of 40mm. This proved to be a fortuitous choice, as the extra compressive strength provided by this thickness of steel was actually required, following the decision to build the wheel horizontally and lift the entire structure in one go — using the legs as a giant pivot. As with the rim sections, the legs were delivered to site fully fitted out, inside and out, with the appropriate fittings, ladders, intermediate work platforms, cable fixing points and, in one, a small mechanical hoist.

Due to the scale of the project and the speed of construction, it had been necessary for Hollandia to subcontract out a good deal of the initial steel fabrication. For a company which prides itself as much on the quality of its workmanship as on its organisational abilities, this was something of a disappointment. To make up for it, however, Hollandia did retain fabrication of one of the most complex elements: the connection at the top of the A-frame legs. The focus of massive forces, both in its final state and during the uplift, this integrates and links a total of three pin-joint assemblies: the permanent support for the hub and the spindle; the smaller anchor point for the top of the main backstay cables; and the anchor point for the cables used to lift the entire structure vertical. The use of very thick steel plates, combined with the complete accuracy required during their fabrication and assembly, transformed what might otherwise have been a purely practical element into something approaching a work of art.

"The initial assumption had always been that the wheel would be built vertically; this is what we had analysed during our work in 1997 for Arups, and it was our starting point when we began work on the project again in September 1998. Very quickly, however, we realised there were real problems with the programme. It would just take too long, because you had to complete the legs and the hub and spindle before you could start the assembly of the rim. And the assembly *itself would be far more time-consuming: controlling the dimensional tolerances would be much more difficult and there were all the problems of working at height. By a strange coincidence, we had just started work on another job, for Mammoet, making special sections for the jib of a lifting gantry capable of lifting up to 3000 tonnes – much heavier than the wheel – and this started us thinking. Building the wheel horizontally brought*

many advantages: the tolerances were much easier to control; it was safer; and it would be much quicker – we could meet the schedule. But there were problems too. We didn't know if we could get planning permission to build over the river; there were financial considerations; and it would mean a total reassessment of the design work we had done so far – we did not know what effect the lift would have on the structure. As it turned out, the rim needed very little new engineering, beyond calculations for

extra support cables to be used during the lift itself. The real impact was on the foundations – they had to be much bigger – and on the legs, particularly the connection at the head of the A-frame where all the lifting forces were concentrated."

Maarten Jongejan
Managing Director, Hollandia BV

The full 1000-tonne load generated by the rim, spoke cables and capsules is transferred to the spindle via two spherical roller bearings, purpose-made for the project by FAG OEM und Handel at its factories at Schweinfurt and Wuppertal in Germany. With inner core diameters of around 2.1 metres, the bearings were more-or-less standard items, the only unusual aspect being the use of drilled rolling elements held in place by a 'cage', rather than allowed to run free. This allows the rollers to be tightly spaced, helping to spread the high loads more evenly.

"We first became involved in this project as long ago as September 1995, when we were approached by Ove Arup & Partners to discuss the relative advantages of different types and sizes of bearings. They already had some ideas for the size of the spindle and we were able to prepare a design for them – a good solution. Then time went by; we transferred the design to FAG Japan but nothing came back, so it was a real surprise when Hollandia came to us with the same project. Fortunately, they had based their design on our dimensions and only a few revisions were required, which allowed us to complete the project very quickly. Of course, every bearing of this size is unique to some degree, but there are set solutions to specific problems, so there is usually a precedent you can refer to. In fact, FAG made some bearings of a similar size around 20 years ago, so we can be confident of this design."

Gerhard Kleine
Production Manager, FAG OEM und Handel AG

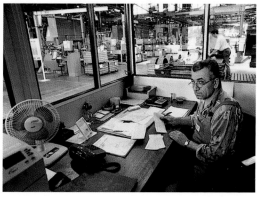

"FAG has been making bearings for more than 100 years, so design now is more a case of evolution than new ideas – improving manufacturing techniques to give the bearings a longer life and so on. It depends on the maintenance, of course, and the general working conditions, but we would expect these bearings to last 50 years with no problems at all. We have bearings far older than that, still in operation"

Klaus Ptácnik
Quality Assurance Manager, FAG OEM und Handel AG

The final assembly of the bearings *(below left)*, each weighing around 6.2 tonnes, was completed at FAG's factory in Wuppertal with the final fitting to the hub castings being carried out at Hollandia *(left and below right)*. Produced in case-hardened steel, the bearing's rolling elements have a gentle convex curve, the radius of which is slightly tighter than the matching concave curve of the raceways, to ensure the load is transferred through a narrow 'contact ellipse' well within the roller's overall width at all times. As might be expected, the tolerances are very small indeed: a mere 2 microns, or 0.002 mm, covering *all* the rolling elements, and around 10 microns for the raceways. Designed with a theoretical lifetime of 200,000 hours operational use — or 50 years, running at the present schedule — and considered all but fail-proof, it was nevertheless decided that allowance should be made to remove one or both bearings while *in situ*, just in case. The inner bearing was therefore made slightly smaller than its outer counterpart, to ensure there was adequate all round clearance should it ever need to be withdrawn past the outer bearing point.

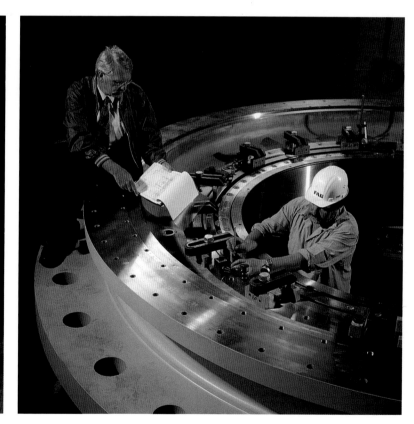

It had been realised at the outset that the only real way to be entirely sure that the spindle was up to the job was to carry out a full-load test before it was transferred to site. With a total imposed load in excess of 1150 tonnes, this was easier said than done. Fortunately, Hollandia had a small assembly hall of just the right size *(right)*, and this was transformed into a full-size test rig. A massive, purpose-made tubular steel frame, complete with fixing straps, held the centre and fixed end of the spindle in place, while further straps attached to hydraulic jacks pulled on the spindle's free end. During the test itself, the loads were increased in steady increments, so that the actual stresses and deflections could be checked against the calculated values at each stage. In this way, any deviation between the figures would pick up any problems well before the spindle was placed at risk. In fact, the figures corresponded almost exactly at every stage.

Below: Peter Koorevaar, Jacques Berenbak, Nardo Hoogendijk and Chiel Smits wait in the test hall as the final preparations are made. Meanwhile, outside on the assembly yard *(bottom)*, the A-frame legs are nearing completion.

"Here we were, nine months into the project and just weeks away from the uplift, and we were deliberately over-stressing the single most critical element on the entire project. Rationally, of course, you knew all the calculations had been done and that it should all work — but you couldn't help feeling a slight risk."

Neil Thompson
Design Manager, Mace Limited

"The last section of the spindle only arrived about 10 days before we were due to do the test, which made it a great rush to get everything ready. It arrived on a Saturday afternoon, after it was stopped in the night twice by the German police, but immediately we moved it into the small assembly hall we were using and tack welded it to the two other sections. Everything had to be surveyed and checked, so it was a long night. But it went well and on Sunday afternoon we started the pre-heating so that the we could begin welding on the Monday morning. The thickness of steel we were welding was around 140mm, much thicker than we had done at Hollandia before, so we brought in a special team of welders with the right experience. They were all people we knew well, people we trusted – we knew the welds had to be perfect the first time. They started with the inside welds which were the most difficult. Because of the pre-heating (around 150˚C) it was very hot inside the spindle, so each man could only work for around 30 minutes before a change over. The welds had to be carried out continuously, working round the clock, but it was all completed on schedule, by the following Friday. Then we had to do all the testing and a final heat treatment to relieve the stresses, leaving only the Monday and Tuesday to complete all the preparations for the test on Wednesday. Then, on Thursday morning, we started the shot blasting."

Martin Broeders
Production Manager, Hollandia BV

Although the spindle performed exactly as predicted, the test itself had more than its fair share of excitement. A nearby lightning strike, some three hours after the test had started, burnt out half the sensors — fortunately, after sufficient data had been gathered to show there were no problems with the spindle itself. Then, the straps imposing the load suddenly slipped on their fixing blocks, causing more than a little consternation among the assembled engineers and observers. This took time to fix and it was close to 4am before the test was successfully completed.

"It was a very strange night. First, there was the storm, then the problems with the testing equipment. And as if that was not enough, I was stopped on the way home by the police. They were on the look-out for drug dealers and wanted to know why I was out so late. They even had a dog check my car for drugs."

Arie Lanser
Project Manager, Iv-Infra

"This might sound rather alarming, but there is a very specific problem, known as brittle fracture, which occurs when you bring thick steel, tensile stress and cold temperatures together — all conditions that occur on the spindle. You don't come across this problem normally, but as you might imagine the consequences can be enormous. The spindle's fracture toughness was therefore a major concern, and it was one of the main reasons we did the load test — though not for the reasons you might imagine. It was useful to check the actual performance against the strength predictions, of course, but there is another far more beneficial reason for doing this type of non-destructive testing, which is to do with any cracks that might be in the material. It has been found that if you deliberately impose tensile stresses on thick steel greater than those it will experience in normal use, any cracks that are there, however small, are pulled open slightly allowing the metal around the end of the crack to expand. This leaves a residual compression around the crack when the load is relaxed, restricting future propogation. The over-stressing improves the toughness."

Allan Mann
Technical Director, Babtie Allott & Lomax

With tolerances measured in fractions of a millimetre, the fitting of the hub over the spindle was always going to be a delicate operation, though this was made easier, to some extent, by a slight tapering of the spindle – stepping down in gradual stages from a diameter of 2100mm, at the inner bearing point, to 2040mm where the outer bearing sits. The two bearings had been sized to match. By 18 June 1999, both the hub and the spindle were complete and the bearing points properly prepared – the 'inner' point *(below)* finished with an area of Teflon coating so that the bearing can 'slide' over the spindle in response to minor deflections and changes in temperature – only the outer bearing is fixed. In a carefully controlled operation, the hub was first manoeuvred over the spindle *(opposite)*. Both bearings were then preheated *(left)*, causing them to expand slightly, so that they could be positioned over their bearing points precisely. The entire operation took a full day and was a complete success on the first attempt.

"As there was no way of guaranteeing that the two bearing points were exactly aligned – the spindle is just too big – it was decided to specify spherical bearings as these allow a slight angular misalignment between the two. With the loads we have here, this is only about half a degree, but as the bearings are so far apart this is plenty. These were our standard design in most respects. The only real change we made was to taper, very slightly, the outside of the bearings' outer rings to make it easier to remove them from the hub, should that ever be necessary. These are normally straight. This was decided quite early on, so that the hub castings could be machined at the same angle."

Gerhard Kleine
Production Manager, FAG OEM und Handel AG

With its tapered legs standing 20 metres apart at their base and measuring well over 60 metres in length, the 310-tonne A-frame was prepared for despatch to London, like the rim sections before it, fully painted and in as complete a state as possible. A temporary boom held the legs apart at the correct distance at their base, while straps supported temporary work platforms along the top of the legs, to allow safe access on site for as long as the A-frame was held at the horizontal. Even the backstay cables that would eventually span between the fixing brackets at the bottom of the legs and the end of the spindle were in place, tied down on the walkways, it being easier to load them now, on dry land, rather than later over the river. Two floating cranes lifted the A-frame clear of the wharf (below), before backing away to allow the main transport barge to be towed into place.

Great care was taken when setting the A-frame down on to the barge, to ensure it was properly aligned and fully supported at every point — an essential precaution if all risk of distortion during the sea crossing was to be avoided.

97

As the A-frame legs and the hub and spindle assembly were to be lifted into place on site on consecutive days, it made sense to transport them to London on the same barge. Programme deadlines were looming and everything was now happening very quickly indeed. The loading was completed in one day, on 28 June 1999, and the barge set sail that night to arrive at its holding point in the Thames Estuary, near the Dartford Tunnel, by the following afternoon. Here, everything was washed down and checked, while ballast was removed from the barge to improve its manoeuvrability during the trip upriver to site. This took place on the very next day and, on the day after that, the A-frame was lifted into place.

L 21,50
B 5,50

Long-time advocates for greater use of the river, Marks Barfield Architects had been determined from the very beginning that the wheel should be situated by the Thames, preferably as close to the centre of London as possible. When the options were considered, Jubilee Gardens on the South Bank stood out immediately as the obvious choice, offering the very best views over the historic heart of the city while continuing a tradition for forward-looking structures on the site that had been established during the 1951 Festival of Britain. And as more detailed research was undertaken *(below)* — into links to public transport and other nearby tourist destinations, as well as studies on the impact to traffic and tourist movements, and so on, by Ove Arup & Partners — the more the correctness of that initial decision was reinforced. There was one restriction, however, imposed by a strategic view of St Paul's Cathedral *(right)*, from a point on the Embankment near Westminster Pier. Strict guidelines forbid the view being blocked by any permanent structure, and the only solution was to build the wheel at the end of Jubilee Gardens nearest County Hall. As it turned out, this was the preferred site and was on land that, for the most part, belonged to the owner and landlord of County Hall, Shirayama Shokusan. The company was enthusiastic and offered its full support.

The Millennium Wheel: Daily Pedestrian Movement

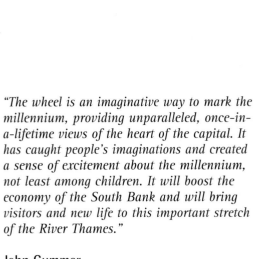

"The wheel is an imaginative way to mark the millennium, providing unparalleled, once-in-a-lifetime views of the heart of the capital. It has caught people's imaginations and created a sense of excitement about the millennium, not least among children. It will boost the economy of the South Bank and will bring visitors and new life to this important stretch of the River Thames."

John Gummer
Secretary of State for the Environment

"The more we found out about the site, the more right it seemed. The practical advantages were clear but, more importantly, there were also strong arguments that it would bring very real benefits to the area. The project could be matched to any number of government and local strategies for the regeneration of that part of London, creating local jobs and helping to draw the wealth of the north bank across the river. Not that there wasn't initial resistance. Lambeth consulted over 100 bodies of various sorts — local and statutory, as well as all of London's 33 boroughs — and over the next two years we spent a lot of time talking to them, explaining our ideas and gradually gaining their support. In the end, the response was overwhelmingly in favour, to the extent that all three chairs on the Lambeth planning committee — there being a hung council at the time — had prepared their own speeches welcoming the project. Even then we could not be sure, as the project could have been called in by the Department of the Environment, but then John Gummer gave it his support, too. Looking back now, in many ways one of the greatest successes of the project lay not so much in the design, nor in finding suitable contractors and manufacturers, but in gaining the necessary permission to build the wheel where we did."

Julia Barfield
Partner, Marks Barfield Architects

103

Work on the Jubilee Gardens site began in February 1999, with the general clearance of the site as a whole and the sinking of the piles that underpin the foundations, many to depths of over 33 metres. Connected by heavy underground beams to act as a single integrated unit, the foundations comprise two main elements: a compression base *(top)*, with 45 piles, to support the wheel's A-frame legs; and a tension base *(above)*, with 12 piles, that provides the fixing point for the main backstay cables. The piling was completed by mid-March, allowing excavation to begin immediately *(right)*.

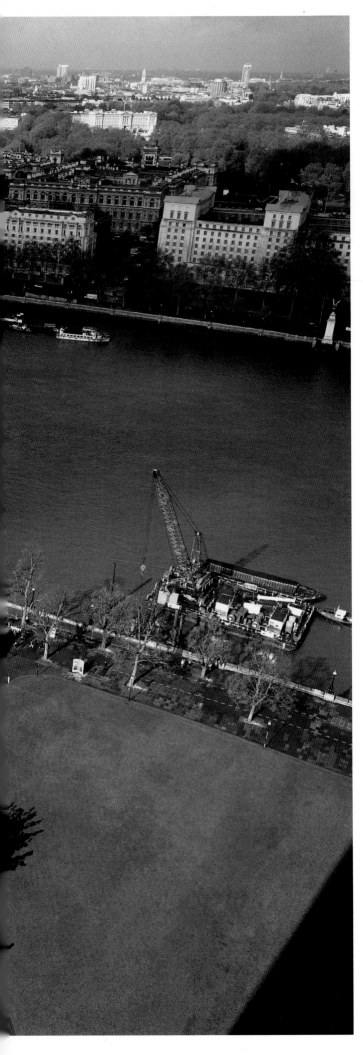

For a variety of reasons — partly to do with ease of construction and partly because it was faster — it had been decided to build the wheel horizontally over the River Thames. Fortunately, this was possible as the site is located on the inside of a curve in the river at that point, and the necessary river works — including a number of temporary platforms to support the structure of the wheel as it was assembled — would not impede the main navigation channel over by the far bank. The civil engineering work itself, which included the preparation of the site, the construction of the main foundations and all the river works, both temporary and permanent, was undertaken by Tilbury Douglas Construction Ltd, a specialist in marine and river works. Appointed under a 'design and construct' contract, Tilbury Douglas selected Tony Gee & Partners to carry out the complex engineering work, while extra support in obtaining the necessary approval and permissions for the works in the river was provided by The Beckett Rankine Partnership.

Work on the river began with the sinking of piled foundations for six of the eight temporary platforms required during the assembly of the rim, and the sinking of permanent foundations alongside The Queen's Walk – with vertical piles for the boarding platform and restraint towers, and large raking piles for the main anchor blocks that now support the landside ends of two pedestrian bridges (or brows) fixed at their far end to a new ferry pier. These brows not only provide access to the pier, but also act as its main mooring points. The anchor blocks, therefore, had to be strong enough to resist the rotational forces imposed by the flow of the river on the pier itself, as well as lateral forces imposed during a possible collision. To avoid any possibility of damage, the ornate Victorian lamp-posts and the carved granite facings of the river wall were carefully dismantled and put into storage for the duration of the works *(bottom right)*, and replaced when the project was complete.

"When we were first approached in October 1998 to submit a tender for the site works, Mace had made it clear that the design was still in its early stages and that the tender was to provide no more than a benchmark price – they knew they had to appoint a contractor sooner rather than later and this was the easiest way. What we hadn't anticipated, however, was just how much the job would grow, and it wasn't really until we were formally appointed in December that the true scope of the work became apparent.

Suddenly, everything changed. There we were, just weeks before we were supposed to start on site, trying to source the extra equipment, check its availability and make sure it would be in place on time. It didn't matter that the engineering work was incomplete; we just had to try and cover every contingency. I don't think any of us had much of a Christmas."

Steve Radcliffe
Divisional Director, Tilbury Douglas Construction Limited

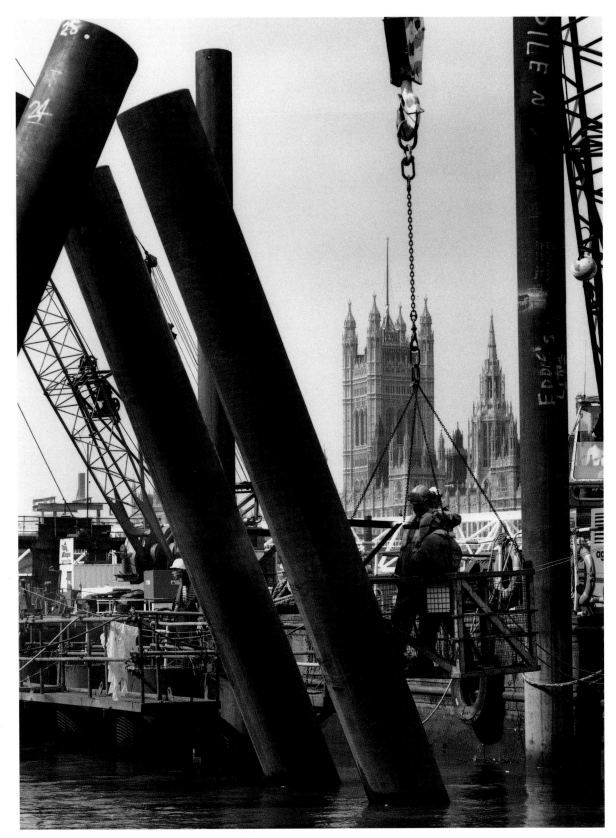

The setting out of the piles and platforms, both temporary and permanent, was carefully monitored at every stage to ensure the structural sections they were designed to support would fit exactly. When possible, much of the surveying, painting and welding was carried out from the shoreline alongside The Queen's Walk *(below)*, which was regularly exposed at low tide.

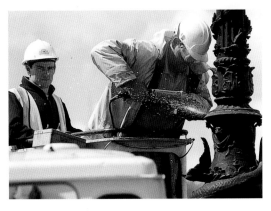

"I came on board in December, just as the job was beginning to gear up. There was the difficulty of trying to establish the size of the piles, so we could bring in the right piling rigs and so on, but there were also a number of concerns about the state of the site. It had a long history, so we weren't really sure what we would find. We sunk some boreholes and checked the archives, but neither method is that accurate. As it turned out, we uncovered part of the foundations for the Dome of Discovery, as well as a section of cobblestone wharf and a large brick cistern that must have been part of a Victorian sawmill. We had some archeologists from the Museum of London on site for a time who unearthed all sorts of smaller remains, some going back to mediaeval times. Even the river bed was surveyed for unexploded ordnance left over from the War."

John Lovell
Contract Manager, Tilbury Douglas Construction Limited

By mid-March, the site had been cleared and a site office erected in the corner closest to Belvedere Road. Incorporating the Mace project office, meeting rooms, a canteen and secondary offices for the various trade contractors, it quickly became the main focal point for everyone involved in the project.

Meetings, formal and informal, planned and unplanned, ebbed and flowed through the confined spaces of the Mace office throughout the day, as members of the different contractors' teams coordinated their operations – an especially important process on a project where site access was so limited.

"Mace's role on the project, ultimately, was to take responsibility for the completion and delivery of the Wheel. We were responsible for the day-to-day activities on site on the one hand, and for the overall strategy on the other – reporting to the client and acting in his interests, but also making sure the relationships between all the subcontractors and all the consultants were as they should be – orchestrating the roles of all the different parties involved, if you will. We had to be able to step in at any point and at any level to ensure everything was happening correctly. Our first contact with the project had actually been to prepare an independent audit for British Airways when they were first considering becoming involved, but even then it had been impossible not to get caught up in discussions over how it might be done. In many ways, with all its technical and operational challenges, it was just the sort of project Mace had been set up to handle. It has certainly been an enormous challenge, probably the biggest we have ever undertaken, but also a tremendous privilege."

Bob White
Managing Director, Mace Limited

108

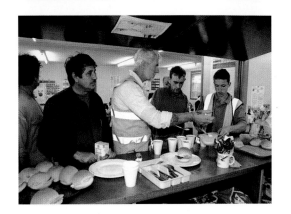

"There seemed to be a great enthusiasm for the project right from the beginning, and this made for an unusually high level of co-operation. We were all part of the same team, and areas of responsibility became blurred as everyone pitched in to help. Everyone was focussed on the same goal and the normal company divides just evaporated."

John Lovell
Contract Manager, Tilbury Douglas Construction Limited

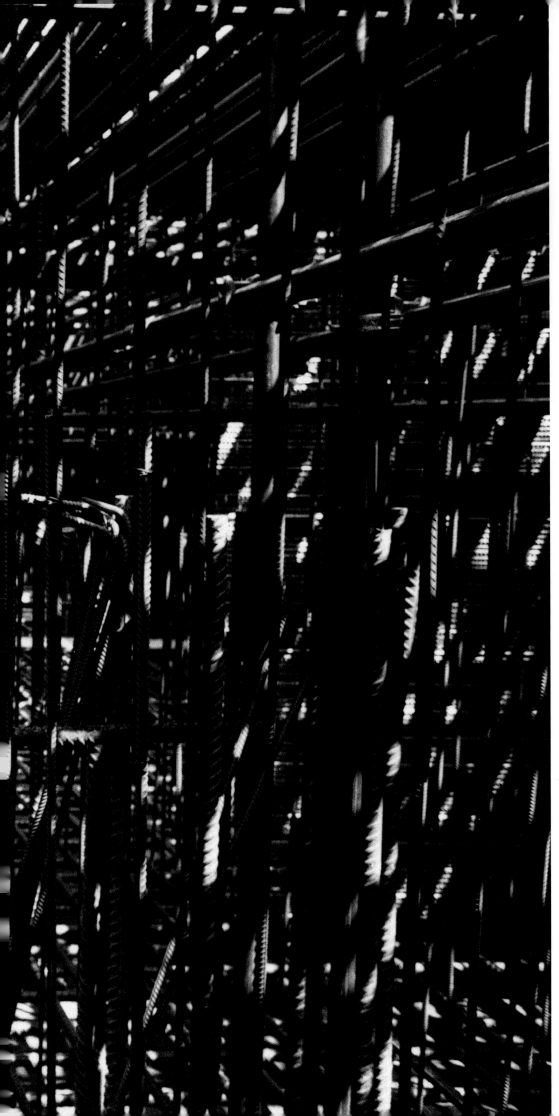

By early April, the excavation of the main foundations for both the compression and tension bases was complete and the setting out of the extensive reinforcement was well under way. Supporting the full 1800-tonne weight of the completed wheel — all transferred down to the ground through the two raking columns that support each of the A-frame legs — the compression base acts as a stiff beam, resisting the 'spreading' load imposed by the splayed legs and transferring the point loads under the columns equally among the piles. Crisscrossed by a dense web of reinforcement bars *(left)* — interlocked with the pile heads below and the reinforcement for the raking columns above — the compression base has more in common with bridge construction than the standard foundation. Incorporating over 180 tonnes of reinforcement, the compression base was split into three equal 'cells' for the pouring of the concrete, each requiring some 800 tonnes. The centre cell was completed first, followed a few days later by the two outer cells, the pours being continuous operations taking up to five hours a time.

Though less massive than the compression base, the tension base *(below)* is an equally impressive structure, requiring great accuracy during the setting out and construction of the tension chamber.

"Tilbury Douglas approached us in October to help with their tender bid, and then appointed us at the beginning of December to prepare designs for all the foundations and river works. Even at that stage it was not entirely clear what the scope of works might be. Iv-Infra were still working on the calculations for the imposed loads during the uplift of the wheel, so we had to come up with an initial design that was flexible enough to be adapted as the final conditions

became known. The most difficult elements were actually the raking columns that support the A-frame. Now that the wheel is erected, they just act as radial struts and give the appearance of straightforward items, but during the uplift, particularly when taking into account the possible dynamic effects due to wind loadings, there were any number of load combinations that had to be considered. We worked closely with the architects to develop a form that was as slender as possible, but that would also accommodate

all the reinforcement we needed while leaving enough space for safe access. It was not easy to resolve but, in a way, that just makes it all the more satisfying to know we came up with a good solution."

Graham Nicholson
Partner, Tony Gee and Partners

May 1999 and as final preparations are made for the pouring of concrete into the compression base *(above)*, the first of the permanent steel shutters for one of the raking columns is made ready for erection *(far left)*. The steel shuttering offered no structural advantage, but was considered the best solution to the problem of combining a high-quality finish with a very compact form. To simplify the issue of access, a full-height 'runway' was installed at the centre of each column to act as a guide for a small platform, on which two workmen could be raised and lowered in complete safety — a particular concern during the pouring of the concrete, which had to be compacted by hand to ensure the quality required. *Left:* Andrew Elliott, John Lovell and Steve Radcliffe discuss progress on site.

"Considering the scale of the project, it was a real postage stamp of a site, especially with so much large equipment about. It was a constant battle to co-ordinate all the overlapping trades — making sure everyone had access to their area of operations at the right time; that they could work safely; and that their deliveries were properly scheduled."

Andrew Elliott
Project Manager, Tilbury Douglas Construction Limited

By Tuesday 15 June, the day that the first rim section *(below)* would be lifted on to site, the pouring of the concrete for the compression base had been completed and the first of the two raking columns had been lifted into place. Erected with a flat back at this stage, a curved cowling would bc wclded to the permanent steel shuttering of the columns at a later date, completing their elegant form and, at the same time, concealing access ladders and supply cables. Out in the river, the support platforms for the rim sections due to arrive in the following weeks are nearing completion, while on site the tension base, with its heavily reinforced tension chamber roof *(right)*, awaits its final concrete pour.

TENSION
BASE

Site Assembly

The arrival of Taklift 1, which was brought up river on Thursday 10 June, signalled a new stage in the development of the project, with a marked shift of emphasis from the prefabrication of the previous months to a new phase focussed primarily on the work in London. One of Europe's largest seagoing floating cranes — or sheerlegs, to use its correct technical term — Taklift 1 is an impressive vessel by any standards. With the main jib raised to its full 45 metre height, it is capable of lifting up to 800 tonnes, while with the standard fly-jib in place — as used on site — it can easily lift 400 tonnes at an outreach of around 20 metres, well within the requirements of this project. By far the largest vessel ever sailed this far up the River Thames, Taklift 1's journey to site was timed with the falling tide to ensure adequate clearance below the various bridges. As a final check, small flags were raised on the outer corners of the leading frame to a position slightly higher than the vessel's highest point, with members of the crew watching to check they cleared the undersides of the bridges.

"The erection process, ultimately, was driven by what size crane you could place on the site. With so much work going on in the river, land-based cranes were no help at all — so it came down to what size rig we had that could travel that far upriver, what its outreach would be, how close could it manoeuvre into the river wall and so on. Hollandia had to work with what we could supply"

Roger Wilson
Contracts Manager, Smit International (UK) Ltd

"We have done a lot of work with Hollandia over the years, so they knew our equipment very well, knew what it could do – what they didn't know about was working on the River Thames. From the loads they were talking about, we knew that Taklift 1 was the only option, which was already a big help because we had used Taklift 1 during the demolition of the old Blackfriar's Bridge some years ago – so we knew reaching that point was not a problem. We had no idea of conditions further upriver, but were able to get the infor-

mation we needed from the PLA (the Port of London Authority). *It turned out the only real problem would be the new Blackfriar's Bridge – the river is shallow there and the bridge has shallow arches. It was critical, but not impossible: we only had to pick our time carefully to match the tide. The clearances were small – only 30 to 40 centimetres above and below – but the real problem was holding everything straight. When everything was folded down, the length from the bow of the lead tug to the stern of the crane barge*

was over 170 metres, and the view from the bridge of Taklift 1 is very limited. We placed tugs either side to control the swing, but all the main decisions had to be made from the lead tug, which is why we insisted we use our own, with our own crew. Like all these operations, the real work is in the planning. If that is done well, then the work on the day should be relatively easy."

Jan Kwadijk
Project Manager, Takmarine BV

119

"One of the key moments on the project for me personally was when that first piece of steel came upriver. Until then, there had always been a nagging doubt that the project could be stopped at any time, but when that first rim section came under Tower Bridge, I knew there was no going back."

David Marks
Partner, Marks Barfield Architects

David Marks, Julia Barfield and family *(left)*, after the trip upriver with the first section.

Realising local expertise was essential when working on the River Thames, Broedertrouw BV — the Dutch company responsible for the safe transport of the individual sections of the wheel — used their own crews only for the main sea crossing from Rotterdam, delivering the barges to a holding point just downriver from the Thames Barrier. Here, responsibility for the barges was transferred to John Beadle of shipping agents Thames & Orwell, who appointed Thames & Medway Towage to carry out all the moves on the river, with additional support from General Marine and barge master Peter Sargent.

"The PLA had known about the project for some time — we had had some general discussions with Marks Barfield Architects at a very early stage — but in practical terms, our first active involvement came when we were approached about the possibility of building the wheel flat in the river. Our position has always been to encourage people to use the river and the port, so we were enthusiastic in principle. It was essential, however, to gauge what was actually possible in a properly safe manner. We decided, therefore, to carry out a trial before work started, setting out a line of buoys to gauge possible problems and that led to local traffic controls being put in place to define clearly a safe navigation channel. Then it was a matter of discussing with Hollandia and Smit International just how large the individual shipments would be, so we could properly plan the moves with our pilots, the local watermen and the support tugs. Taklift 1 was by far the biggest 'lump', but the rim sections had their own problems, too, mainly because of the way they hung over their barges. As ever, it came down to planning for every contingency — from having Railtrak personnel on hand to stop the trains should we hit one of their bridges to knowing where we could moor if we missed the tide. On the day, the moves themselves went so smoothly they were almost boring — which was wonderful!"

David Cartlidge
Harbour Master, Port of London Authority

121

The River Thames has a long tradition as a working river, but nowadays most larger vessels only have access to the Pool of London, above Tower Bridge, as movement beyond that point is restricted by the headroom of the bridges further upstream. Working closely with the Taklift team, however, Hollandia knew it would be possible to sail the one-quarter rim sections through to the site as long as the moves were timed to coincide with the right tides. Even then, clearance below Southwark Bridge *(below)* was critical, with its shallow arches reducing the available headroom to as little as 40 centimetres. Working closely with pilots from the Port of London Authority, barge master Peter Sargent — who sat on top of the rim sections as they passed under the lowest bridges — and the tug crews from Thames & Medway and General Marine were able to deliver every section to site safely.

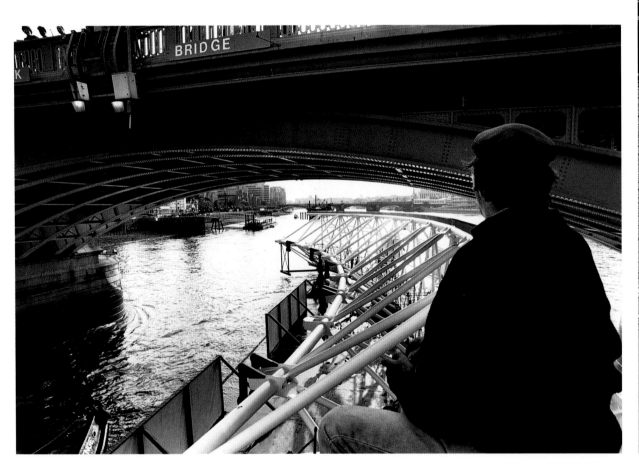

The sideways swing of the barges had to be carefully controlled not only as the rim sections passed under the lowest bridges *(above)* — to ensure there was sufficient clearance, first on one side, then the other — but also in the short distance between London and Southwark Bridges *(right)*, where the tidal flow is disturbed.

"There have been Sargents working on the river for more than 200 years. My great-great-grandfather was a Thames Waterman, operating out of Southwark, and my father and his seven brothers were all Watermen, too. But things have changed enormously in the last 30 years and now there is only my cousin and I from our generation, with only my son to take over after us. Hopefully, the tradition will continue, as you will always need people who know the river well, have the experience. The river is changing all the time and you have to learn its ways, where it can catch you out. The key thing with moving the rim sections was to use the tides. We were working with a 'dumb' barge, of course, and this would want to swing, but that can be controlled with the right number of tugs. If the tides weren't right, on the other hand, you were stuck. Hollandia had clearly done their homework and had timed all the movements to fall on the fortnightly spring tides when the river is both at its highest and its lowest. The currents are stronger, but it meant there was enough of a drop to give us the clearance we needed at every bridge. Of course, the tide charts are only a guide. The weather — if it has been raining, if it is high or low pressure and so on — all have an effect, but the PLA had posted a man at Tower Pier who could provide accurate readings when we needed them."

Peter Sargent
Licensed Waterman, Sargent Brothers

"Our biggest problem with nearly all the work on the river, but especially with the main lifts, was timing everything to coincide with the high tides. Taklift and the barges were moored well out in the main flow where we could work at any time, but once you started to move inshore time was always very limited. Before any operation, we had to be very sure we could complete the work in time – to bring the section into position, lower it exactly, disconnect all the chains and shackles, and then move out before the tide fell too far. It didn't help that the tides changed so much. Most of the big lifts, like the first rim sections and, later, the A-frame and hub and spindle, were timed to coincide with the high spring tides to give us a bigger leeway. But this only allowed four or five days – if we had missed the dates the work would have been delayed for at least two weeks. This was especially critical with the first rim section, as Taklift 1 had to move in very close to the river wall where it was particularly shallow. And, of course, we hadn't done this before, so we weren't really sure how long each part of the operation would take. As it turned out, the rim sections were well balanced and we had good supports in place, so the work went very smoothly."

Jan Stam
Site Operations Manager, Hollandia BV

The on-site assembly of the main elements that make up the structure of British Airways London Eye began with the lifting of the first one-quarter rim section on Tuesday 15 June. Using a system of strategically placed mooring lines, Taklift 1's experienced crew could swing the sheerlegs into position with almost pin-point accuracy, even when working against the current of the river. The only major concern was a cooling water outlet from the Shell Building, which projected from the river bed, just down river from the site, and had to be avoided at all times by both the crane barge and its mooring lines.

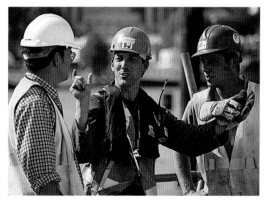

Far left: Jan Stam, Hollandia's site construction manager, and his right-hand man Jacob van der Meulen *(left)* oversee the final preparations.

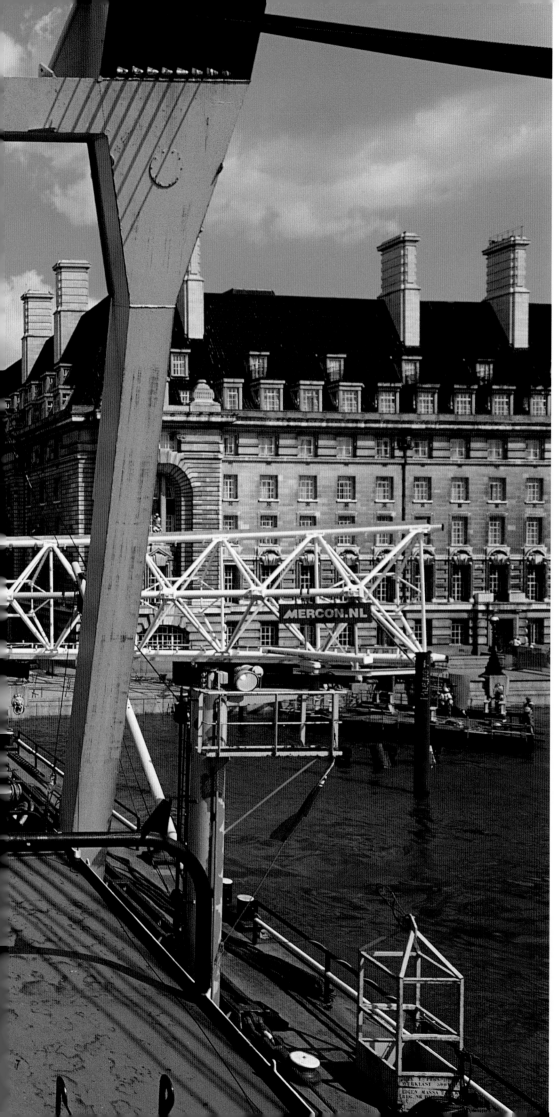

Timed to coincide with the high tide – so as to allow a safe draught beneath Taklift 1 as it worked close to the riverbank – the first rim section was lifted on to temporary supports that had previously been carefully aligned along Queen's Walk. Just as the rim sections themselves had been built to very tight tolerances, the final assembly, too, required total accuracy and the whole operation was monitored continually by a surveying team from the Dutch specialist Delta Surveys. Responsible for every stage of the assembly and uplift, they ensured that the section was lowered within the set guidelines. Even though working at close to its furthest outreach for the load it was carrying (around 144 tonnes), the Taklift crew were able to position the rim section well within the tolerances allowed. Hydraulic jacks were then used for the final accurate positioning.

In the week following the positioning of the first rim section, two further rim sections were brought up river and lifted into position, this time on to temporary platforms over the river (opposite). The rim section on the upstream side nearest Westminster Bridge was located first, followed by the section opposite The Queen's Walk and furthest out in the river. As before, each operation was closely monitored by Jan Stam and the team from Delta Surveys (below right). Final welding started as soon as the rim sections were properly aligned, followed by weld testing (bottom) and painting (right). Because it had been necessary to manoeuvre Taklift 1 within the circle of the rim while the first rim sections were lifted, the central platform required to support the hub and spindle could only be positioned once this work was completed. Piling had already been discounted due to the weight the platform would have to support. Instead, at Hollandia's suggestion, it was built on a barge, which was now towed into position and deliberately sunk on to a levelled stone base, prepared earlier, on the river bed.

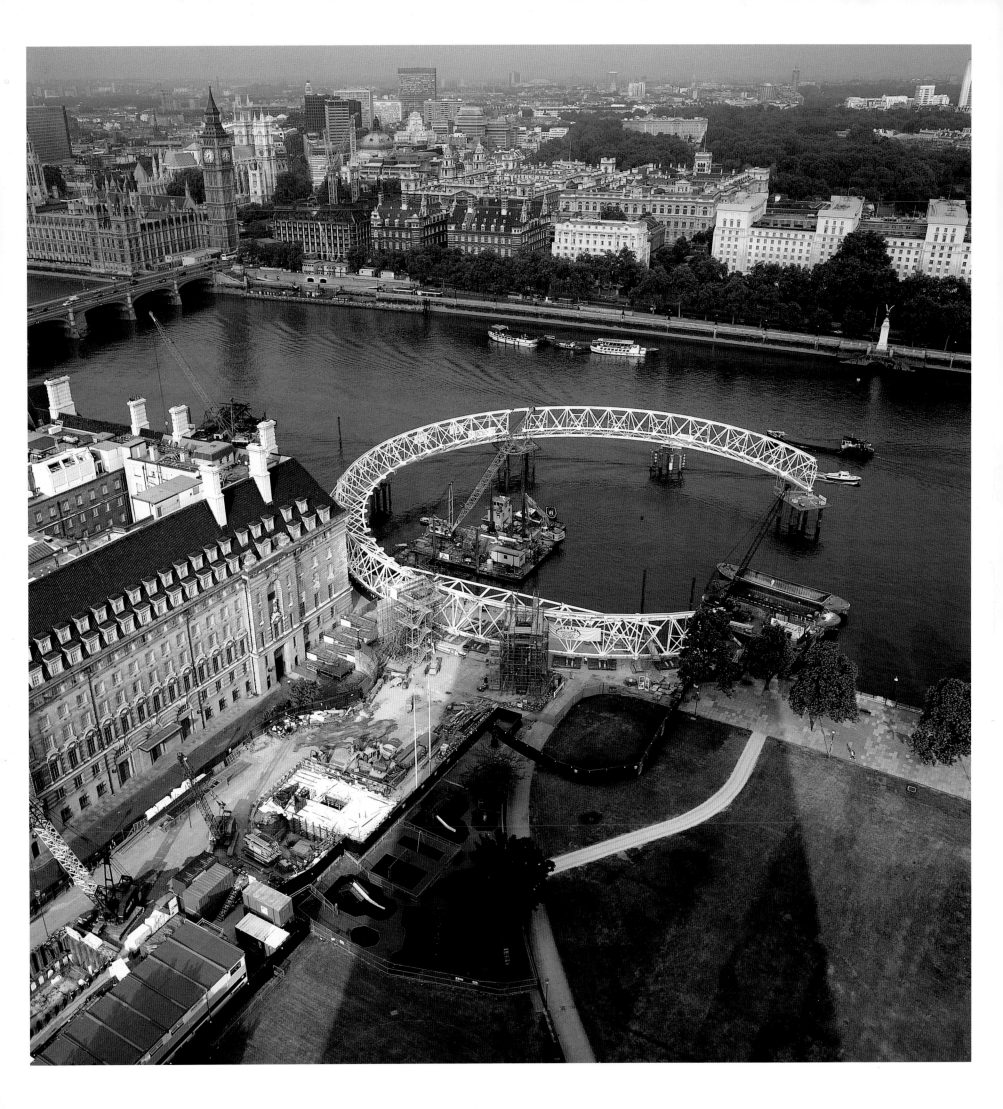

Connected at its base by pin-joint connections with tolerances measured in a few millimetres, the final surveying and positioning of both the cast steel feet atop the raking columns and the central platform out in the river had to be carried out with extreme accuracy to ensure the massive A-frame legs would fit exactly. At this stage, the raking columns were still wrapped in scaffolding, partly to allow access and partly because their permanent steel shuttering was still awaiting shot blasting and its final coats of paint. On the day of the lift, Taklift 1 made light work of manoeuvring the A-frame into position, and all the careful surveying paid off when the pin-joint 'flanges' at the foot of each leg dropped snugly into place. Temporary pins allowing a degree of movement were inserted *(bottom left)* to hold the legs in place during the fitting of the hub and spindle. Only when that operation was complete, and the whole structure properly aligned, were these removed and the permanent stainless-steel pins *(bottom right)* fitted in their place.

The scale of this job is such that you have to think about things you wouldn't normally worry about. The A-frame legs, for example, are so long that even a modest load will cause them to contract a bit. It is not difficult to work out — it's around 20mm now the wheel is complete — but it had to be taken into account."

Allan Mann
Technical Director, Babtie Allott & Lomax

"We couldn't be entirely sure just how much the the central support and its barge would settle after the loads had been put in place. The combined weight of the hub and spindle assembly and the A-frame legs was well in excess of 600 tonnes so we had to assume the barge would sink into the river bed by a significant amount, even if the stone base we had laid would help spread the load. In fact, it ended up settling around 600mm, but fortunately this was within the scope of the hydraulic jacks installed by Hollandia to correct the difference."

John Lovell
Contract Manager, Tilbury Douglas Construction Limited

By the time the A-frame legs were lifted into position, all foundation work on the tension and compression bases had been completed. Out on the river, the base frame of the boarding platform, painted white, was already in position alongside The Queen's Walk, and work was continuing on the raking foundation piles that now support the landside end of the brows leading to the new ferry pier. Just before the lift commenced, members of the assembly team — from Hollandia, the Mace site office and the Taklift crew — lined up in front of the hub and spindle for a group portrait *(bottom right)*, mirroring a photograph taken more than a century before that had recorded the same moment during the erection of Walter Bassett's Great Wheel in Blackpool *(top right)*.

Carefully timed so that the final positioning coincided with the mid-afternoon high tide, the hub and spindle was lifted clear of its transport barge (right) well before noon, allowing plenty of time for Taklift 1 to manoeuvre itself carefully alongside the central support platform. To simplify the operation, the hub and spindle was lowered on to Teflon coated plates some 500mm forward of the A-frame legs and positioned accurately later using hydraulic jacks.

At 335 tonnes — only slightly less than the 'dry' weight of one of British Airways' Boeing 747-400s — the completed hub and spindle assembly was the single heaviest component shipped to London and lifted into place on site. It arrived with its own support frame fitted to one end, which not only formed the base on which the whole assembly would stand during the fitting of the spoke cables, but also helped to hold the hub in place during the lifting operation, and thereby avoid excessive lateral loads on the bearings. As was to happen on so many key moments during the wheel's assembly and uplift, the day of the lift was blessed with near perfect weather: with clear skies, warm sunshine and almost no wind.

The lifting of the last of the major structural elements was timed to coincide with the high spring tides at the beginning of July, a necessary precaution as Taklift 1 had to work close in to the shore. The rhythm of the tides allowed a five day period of opportunity. The A-frame legs were lifted first, on Thursday 1 July, followed the next day by the hub and spindle. A temporary yellow access bridge, spanning between the top of the spindle and the rim, was positioned over the weekend and one final river platform — to support the centre of the last rim section — sunk into place on a barge. With the Monday given over to surveying and final adjustments, the wheel was finally closed with the positioning of the final rim section *(main spread)* on Tuesday 6 July.

"The decision to build the wheel horizontally was presented at our first big meeting with the client team in September 1998. We knew enough about the fabrication by that time to know that trying to complete the wheel by December 1999 was just not possible if we had to build vertically – you had to raise the A-frame and the hub and spindle before any real work could begin on the rim, and there just wasn't time. Apart from all the practical advantages, building the wheel horizontally allowed work to be carried out in parallel, which saved us at least a month – if not two. With our experience of moving other large structures, we knew that the weights we were dealing with would not be a problem in themselves, but going in that direction would clearly have a major effect on the way we designed the structure. We knew building horizontally was a good solution, but it was only possible if we could use the river – and until we knew if this would be allowed, we had no idea which way the design should proceed. We really needed an answer as quickly as possible."

Peter Koorevaar
Technical Director, Hollandia BV

Following the lifting of the last of the main structural sections, a full overall survey of the wheel was carried out and the different elements positioned precisely, allowing the final welding to begin and the permanent pins to be inserted in their respective pin-joint connections. With everything in place, work could then commence on the next major operation: the fixing of the spoke and rotation cables. Unsurprisingly, for a structure where many construction procedures had never been attempted before, the introduction of each new operation was greeted with varying degrees of uncertainty. It often took a few days to refine working procedures that had looked straightforward on paper, and so it was with the fitting of the spoke cables. During the weekend of the final lifts, Hollandia had positioned a temporary access bridge spanning between the top of the spindle and the rim *(left)*, to help with the lifting of the spoke cables. Unfortunately, the system proved unwieldy in practice and the first cables were not fitted *(below)* until late July.

"I can still remember clearly that first big meeting with Hollandia in Rotterdam, when they said they would like to propose a new erection method. The whole team was there, all the usual suspects, looking at these drawings that showed the wheel laid out across the river. None of us said very much, other than to say we weren't really sure about it. We moved on to other issues, but when we left there was a definite feeling that this might be the end of the project. But then, on the the train back to Amsterdam, we were sitting there huddled across the centre aisle chatting about it, and the more we talked, the more we thought it might just be possible — maybe we could close the river when we needed. By the time we reached Amsterdam the mood had changed completely, from a real low to a real high. It was certainly an interesting trip and, somehow, it seemed to set the pattern for the year to come."

Andrew Potter
General Manager, The Tussaud's Group

"Cables have been made in the same way for many, many years, so much of the engineering work is now well understood – the calculations can be very lengthy but performance can normally be predicted with great accuracy. The real challenge is in understanding the dynamic effects due to wind loadings. There are two main conditions to consider: the effects of vortex shedding, where the wind causes resonant vibrations to build up in the cable – this is normally solved using standard Stockbridge dampers – and an effect known as wind and rain 'galloping', which occurs when rain-water collects on the cable and forms a rivulet down one side. This moves as the cable moves and amplifies the vibration. Usually the rivulets are broken up by winding an extra raised wire along the length of the finished cable, but we were worried this might be damaged due to the constant flexing on the wheel. As it happened, there was an alternative solution we had been thinking about for some time, which involved spinning thinner strands into the final layer of the cable to form spiralling grooves. We knew it was a good solution, but it was a bit of a gamble to use them on the wheel as such a design had never been used before in practice. As it turns out, they are working very well."

Massimo Marini
Technical Director, Tensoteci s.r.l.

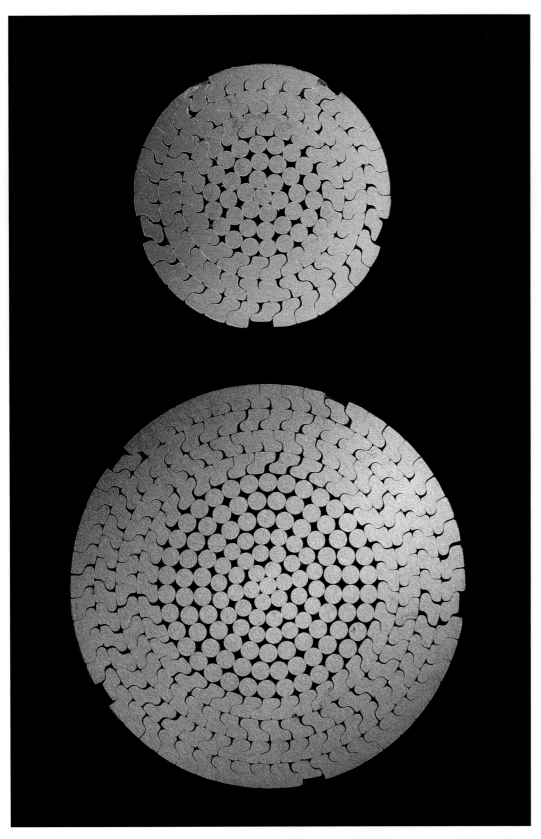

All the cables for the project were manufactured by the Italian company Tensoteci s.r.l. at their Redaelli factory near Milan. Varying in diameter from 60mm for the rotation cables to 110mm for the main backstays, each cable is made up of individual strands — circular at the centre and 'S-shaped' to the outside — spun in layers around a central core in a carefully controlled operation that ensures each layer is tightly bound to its neighbour. Shown left, at true size, are sections through two of the cables used on the wheel: a 70mm spoke cable, made up of 121 strands in six layers, and a 110mm backstay, with 303 strands and 10 layers.

Right: Giuliano Ambroset, Duoc Tu Thanh and Massimo Marini review the performance characteristics of the cables at Tensoteci's main office in Cologno Monzese.

"The general design conditions for the different cables were specified by Hollandia, but the detail design, the choice of dimensions, the fatigue calculations, the dynamic analysis and so on were all carried out by Tensoteci. If there were any concerns about the use of cables, they lay in their reaction to dynamic wind loads: whether vibrations in the cables would cause discomfort for the passengers in the capsules. In the same way that we verified the design of the main structure, we therefore asked the Engineering Office of the City of Rotterdam — who have good experience in solving the problems of cable vibrations — to review Tensoteci's proposals and, where necessary, make their own recommendations. The final design seems to be very successful and, if anything, vibrations in the cables are even lower than expected."

Chiel Smits
Project Manager, Hollandia/Mercon Steel Structures BV

The basic techniques employed in the making of cables — winding layers of individual strands around a central core, the first layer spiralling one way and the second the other — have remained essentially unchanged for more than 100 years. Certainly, many of Tensoteci-Redaelli's winding machines, including the one shown here spinning the main 110mm backstays, have been in use for 40 years or more. This is not to say advances have not been made, but in recent years these have been mainly in the better understanding of the engineering principles and in subtle refinements, notably the introduction of the 'S-shaped' strands that make up a cable's outer layers. Tensoteci are, therefore, rightly proud of their own innovation: the introduction of narrower strands to create grooves in the cable's outer surface. Manufactured in continuous lengths, several hundred metres long, the completed cables were first transferred to a purpose-designed 'runway' where they were stretched to their full working load and cut to length — all this after several stretches at higher loads had been applied to ensure all non-elastic deformations had been removed. In a final operation *(see previous page)*, their final connections were then drawn over the cables and fixed at each end.

"I am not sure if I should tell you this, but we did lose one of the main backstay cables when the lorry transporting it from Italy collided with a bridge. Fortunately, we had already decided to make a spare cable of each type — three, in fact, for the spoke cables — so there was no delay and a new spare has now been made."

Adry Zondervan
Quality Assurance Manager, Hollandia BV

Measurements made during the tests included the creep in the fittings as the initial loads were applied *(left)*, and the stretch in the cables, over a standard two-metre control length, at each of the pre-set load conditions *(far left)*.

"Tensoteci appointed us to carry out the usual range of destructive and non-destructive tests on a sample of each of the cables used on the wheel, not so much to provide data to help in the design process – modern cables are designed very accurately nowadays – but more as a way of providing an independent verification of their calculations. The cables were supplied in lengths of around five metres, complete with their standard fittings, which allowed us to measure the amount of creep in the fittings as well as determine

each cable's modulus of elasticity. We followed an established procedure, increasing the load in 5 per cent increments between 10 and 50 per cent of the cable's predicted minimum breaking load – the usual working load for a cable being normally around 40 per cent of its breaking point. To make sure each cable was completely 'bedded in', with all the strands aligned and binding properly, it was stressed and relaxed for five cycles at each load, establishing a stable working condition where the modulus of

elasticity was constant. When we were happy that this had been accurately recorded, we then moved on to the final stage, loading the cable to its full breaking point. The engineering of modern cables is so good that this normally occurs within a few per cent of the predicted loads, though a few of the external strands may give way first."

Friedrich Dürrer
Head of Test Bay, DMT Gesellschaft für Forschung und Prüfung

Samples of each of the types of cable used on the wheel were tested in Germany at the DMT Institute — a notified testing body for the non-destructive and destructive testing of all forms of ropes and cables — on purpose-built machines capable of applying loads of 2000 tonnes or more, certainly far greater than the loads applied to any of the London Eye's cables. The loads are so great, in fact, that the machines are mounted on their own foundations set into bedrock and the test-hall built around them independently. A closely monitored sequence of non-destructive tests was carried out first — the testing of one of the 90mm back-stays is shown here — after which the cable was enclosed in protective steel covers and loaded to breaking point. For obvious safety reasons, this last operation was monitored from a heavily re-inforced control room (above).

"The strength of the cables is not in question. Predicting their life, however, is a little more difficult. With the main backstay cables, where the load conditions are more or less constant, we can safely predict a life of 50 years with good maintenance. For the spoke and rotation cables, however, we are predicting around 20 to 25 years — though this will be monitored closely."

Massimo Marini
Technical Director, Tensoteci s.r.l.

147

"Of all the lifts we had to make during the assembly of the wheel, those for the cables were actually the most problematic. With all the big sections, it was mainly a matter of connecting them to the crane and balancing them correctly, after which the crane did all the work. With the cables, all the lifting had to be done by hand, using secondary cables, hand winches and chain-blocks. Finding good fixing points for the winches took time and the scaffolding was never where you wanted it. It did not help, either, that the temporary 'flyover' bridge we had installed did not work as well as we had hoped – again, it relied on too many winches, which just took too long to rig and adjust. It did the job, but it was very slow – so we had to work out another method, here on site, that could work in parallel. That is when we decided to use an extra barge, specially adapted for the job, on to which we could load the cables and then float them under the wheel to where they were required. This worked well but now we were reliant on the tides, so it could not be used all the time. It was very frustrating and the entire operation ended up taking far longer than we had planned."

Jan Stam
Site Operations Manager, Hollandia BV

By the beginning of August the fitting of the spoke cables was progressing, though not as smoothly as had been hoped. The problems involved in lifting the cables horizontally while avoiding excessive bending — which could cause irreparable damage — was proving more difficult to solve than first imagined, and the temporary 'flyover' bridge (right) that was meant to make the job easier was too slow. To speed up the operation, Hollandia decided to introduce an alternative fixing method, lifting the cables directly from a barge floated into position beneath the wheel (bottom left). Weighing around 3.4 tonnes each, complete with all their fittings, the cables were first pin-jointed at the hub, then the far end pulled into its appropriate fixing bracket on the rim where it was secured with a threaded collar (below).

Jacob van der Meulen oversees the fitting of a spoke cable from a platform on the 'fly-over' bridge.

The fitting of the spoke and rotation cables was eventually completed towards the end of August, some weeks later than planned but otherwise with complete success. Measuring some 53 metres in length, there are 64 spoke cables in all, 32 spanning radially from each of the hub castings to alternate, equally spaced fixing brackets along the rim's inner chord. As each cable was fitted, a modest tension was introduced to hold the cable horizontal. Later, once all the cables were in place, this was then increased — in a carefully balanced operation which ensured the central hub and spindle was not pulled out of place — to the cables full working load of around 75 tonnes. When the wheel is vertical the weight of the rim is naturally carried by the lower cables alone, reducing the tension in the upper cables. In a high wind, therefore, there is an increased risk that the cables on the leeward side of the wheel might go slack, allowing increased movement around the connections with the potential for irreparable damage. The pretensioning precludes such a situation occurring. A further 16 rotation cables, each 60mm in diameter, were also positioned at this stage. Running at an angle to the spoke cables to fixing positions on the outside of the rim, these ensure there is no lag between the turning of the rim and the turning of the hub.

"At the time the hub castings were designed, we were still assuming the rim would be supported by just 32 cables, working in pairs. This was eventually changed to 64 individual cables, which doubled the number of pin-joint connections at the hub. Fortunately, the castings had flanges large enough to accommodate these without changing the design. Sometimes you need a little luck."

Professor Jacques Berenbak
Senior Design Engineer, Hollandia BV

"The amount of available space in the fixing brackets on the rim was quite limited, so the tolerances set for the lengths of both the spoke and rotation cables was really very small – no more than plus or minus 50mm. As the expected creep in the cables during their lifetime will probably be around 20mm, it was best to work to the low side, and considerable care had to be taken when stretching the cables at the factory, and then cutting them to their correct working length, to make sure the they were fully bedded in and variables such as the temperature had been taken into account. We had decided at the outset to fit permanent strain gauges within the pin-joint connections of each cable, in part to monitor the load changes as the wheel rotates – which will help confirm our fatigue calculations – but also, and more importantly, to check that even under the worst conditions none of the cables ever goes slack. As it turned out, the sensors had an added benefit, as we were now able to monitor the loads on the cables not only during the pre-tensioning – which allowed us to ensure the overall loads remained balanced at all times – but also later, during the uplift."

Massimo Marini
Technical Director, Tensoteci s.r.l.

All major policy decisions were discussed and implemented by a steering group which met most Friday mornings either at the British Airways offices in Buckingham Palace Road *(above)* or, more occasionally, on site *(opposite)*. Made up of representatives of the project's three partners — British Airways, Marks Barfield Architects and The Tussaud's Group — as well as senior members of the Mace project management team, attendance varied slightly through the year but included *(from left to right),* with apologies to those not shown here, Malcolm Cook, Andrew Potter, Ian Crockford, Paul Baxter, Adrian Mahon *(above),* Philip Taylor *(below),* Brian Phipps, Peter Carson and Tim Renwick.

"I think one of the real strengths of the project was that it was just so diverse – there were so many disciplines involved and areas to be considered, that it really was impossible for any one person to have control. Every decision had to be made through consultation, and always there was the constant challenge of having to prove your point, of convincing you peers that your views were the right ones. In many ways it was a true collective, made up of an extraordinary group of people: all powerful characters, all of whom had very strong views about the project, all drawing from different experiences and cultures, but all combined by this shared enthusiasm for the project. The balancing of commercial pressures and idealism was not always easy to resolve and there were more than a few heated moments. The constant discussion and analysis – paralysis on occasion – was frustrating for all of us, but in a very real sense it was this process that has made the wheel the success it is.

Nothing was taken for granted, everything was questioned. Of course, there are those who believe there were too many compromises, but considering the commercial pressures, all the problems of completing the project in such a short time, the level of quality we have achieved is far greater than anyone might have expected."

Andrew Potter
General Manager, The Tussaud's Group

The Netherlands has a long association with companies that specialise in heavy lifting, and it was Hollandia's personal experience of this field that first led them to consider building the wheel horizontally. With a total weight of around 1200 tonnes at the time of the lift, British Airways London Eye is relatively light when compared with lifts achieved elsewhere, but it is particularly unwieldy. Its large diameter made it impossible to lift vertically from the centre, while its height when upright ruled out any chance of lifting at the rim. By chance, in the months preceding their involvement in the wheel, Hollandia had been commissioned by Mammoet Engineering, a specialist in heavy lifting operations, to make special sections for a very large mobile 'crane' — actually a sliding gantry — that was more than capable of handling the loads involved. Working together, Hollandia and Mammoet devised a lifting strategy that involved raising the boom of the sliding gantry upright over the same raking columns that support the permanent A-frame legs of the wheel, to form a second temporary A-frame, and then hauling the wheel upright with cables fixed securely to the massive pin-joint connecting the legs to the spindle. Pulling the wheel upright at an angle — effectively rotating it around the pin-joints at the foot of its A-frame legs — meant that the full load on the cables as the wheel came clear of its supports would exceed 1900 tonnes, but this was well within the system's capabilities.

The unique advantage of Mammoet's sliding gantry is that the entire system has been designed to be broken down and transported in pieces no larger, or heavier, than a standard container. Arriving in sections over several days at the beginning of August (above), the main boom began to take shape on supports set out across nearly the full length of the site (left).

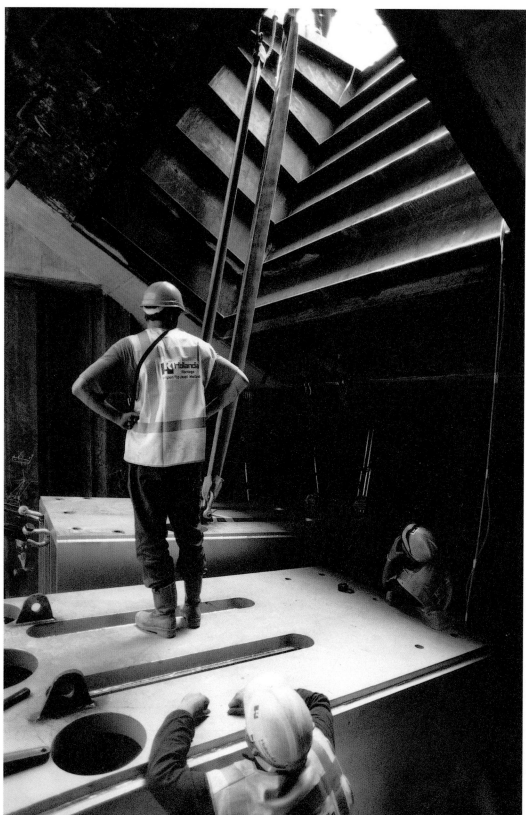

While the Mammoet A-frame began to take shape on the site above, preparation work was proceeding rapidly in the tension chamber below, commencing with the fitting of the steel anchor blocks *(above)*, which had been designed to support both the permanent backstays of the wheel itself and the guide-plates that support the Mammoet A-frame.

With the anchor blocks in place — fixed precisely to the ceiling of the tension chamber — the jacking systems required to draw down and support the main backstays were lifted and bolted into place *(below)*. At the same time, atop the raking columns *(bottom left)*, high-strength grout was injected beneath the cast-steel feet that support the permanent A-frame to form a solid base capable of resisting the extremely high forces imposed during the uplift.

"We were approached by Hollandia in February 1999, initially to do no more than supply and pre-tension the auxiliary cables, required during the uplift to provide extra support to the rim. Mammoet had no time to do the work themselves but, as we supply their strand-jacks, they suggested Hollandia speak to us directly. The lift procedures were still being finalised at that stage and it soon became clear that there were, in fact, several other areas where our experience with hydraulic jacks and control systems would come in useful — particularly as for most of the work we would be working alongside Mammoet, integrating our two control systems. Within a few weeks, the scope of the work doubled to take in not just the auxiliary cables, but also a complete stability system for the rim and a secondary jacking system to draw the main backstays down into the tension base as the uplift proceeded. We ended up installing two sets of jacks in the tension base: a permanent set mounted directly on the steel anchor block to hold and adjust the backstays once they were supporting the full weight of the wheel; and a secondary lighter set, mounted behind the main jacks, to actually draw the cables down during the lift."

Tjerko Jurgens
Managing Director, Hydrospex Cylap BV

Due to the extremely large loads and dimensions involved, the uplift itself was carried out using four hydraulic strand-jacks *(below)* fixed to the top of the Mammoet A-frame. Capable of lifting 600 tonnes each – the load being spread across 36 individual strands, each 140 metres long – the jacks work in tandem and automatically balance the overall load between them as the strands are drawn in. The A-frame, the jacks and the purpose-built 'head' that guides the free ends of strands out of the way, after they have been drawn in, was assembled as a complete unit while still lying horizontally across the site – the strands themselves being fitted after the base of the Mammoet A-frame had been raised up and placed on special castings fixed to the top of the raking columns *(opposite)*. Positioned over the pin-joint connections that support the bottom of each of the wheel's A-frame legs, these temporary castings – made specifically for this one operation by Skoda – held the base of the Mammoet A-frame in place as it was swung upright into its final working position.

"As the design engineer in charge of erection procedures, it was my role to co-ordinate between Hollandia, Mammoet and Hydrospex and decide which company would be responsible for each part of the operation. It all came about, of course, because we were actually making special parts for the second of Mammoet's large sliding gantries, though I wouldn't say that was the reason we thought of building the wheel horizontally – there were a number of other benefits with that approach. Once that decision was made, however, it was clear that the Mammoet system, and in particular the boom we were making, might offer a good solution. We approached Mammoet to check if the boom might be available in June and they replied that it was – as long as we completed the work on time. From that point on, we started to work out how the job could be done."

Nardo Hoogendijk
Design Engineer, Hollandia BV

"One of the biggest problems with the uplift was that the highest forces occurred at the first moment of the lift. The critical point was at the top of the 11-metre high raking columns, where the horizontal forces imposed through the permanent A-frame and the vertical forces from the Mammoet A-frame above were transferred down into the columns themselves. We had considered supporting the Mammoet A-frame at ground level, but it was actually more efficient to stand this on the columns as well, so that its vertical load combined with the horizontal forces imposed during the uplift to create a resultant force acting at 65 degrees, which was much easier to sustain."

Nardo Hoogendijk
Design Engineer, Hollandia BV

Before the Mammoet A-frame was lifted upright, the pin-jointed guide-line plates connecting the top of the frame to the tension base — and thereby preventing the entire structure falling forward into the river — were folded and positioned underneath the strand-jacks (*opposite*).

Following a site visit by Bob Ayling (*bottom left*), two very large mobile cranes were brought on to the site and the head of the A-frame raised sufficiently (*below right*) to allow the strand-jacks to take up the slack and complete the lift themselves.

"*Mammoet introduced the first very large sliding gantry some two years ago, so we have built up a good experience of its use in normal operations — of its standard assembly procedures and so on. In fact, one of the attractions of this project was that it was so different; it was interesting to explore just what the standard equipment was capable of. As it turned out, the uplift itself was the least of our worries: the maximum imposed load on the system at the moment the rim lifted clear of its supports was no* more than around 1900 tonnes, well below the capacity of our strand-jacks, while the boom itself can accommodate compression loads of up to 4500 tonnes. Our real problem was assembling the system on such a restricted site. Normally we have the site to ourselves and we would expect to assemble and raise the boom in a matter of days. Here, we had to plan our operations very carefully and co-ordinate with a number of other trades; the times when we had access turned out to be quite limited; and, of course, some of the work had to be carried out over the river. In the end, it took us three weeks just to complete the assembly. Then, there were a few problems raising the boom to vertical — again because of the small site. After that, at least from our point of view, the uplift itself was quite straightforward.*"

Ronald Hoefmans
Project Engineer, Mammoet Engineering & Innovation BV

Dawn on Friday 10 September and the first rays of the early morning sun warm the facade of the Houses of Parliament on the opposite bank *(above)*, while leaving the completed structure of British Airways London Eye *(main spread)* in shadow. All the necessary preparations for the uplift were now complete: the final checks on the structure and lifting systems had been made and a beautifully sunny day with only mild winds had been forecast. Within the hour, the uplift was underway. Unfortunately, the day did not turn out quite as planned.

Among those enjoying the almost carnival atmosphere around Jubilee Gardens during the early stages of the uplift were Kate Hoey MP *(top right)* and Bob Ayling *(top)*, while Paul Baxter *(above)* and David Marks and Julia Barfield *(right)* were on hand to answer questions from the press.

"The uplift was safe, but we working close to the limits of what was possible. We needed the best machinery, the best weather, the best people and the best preparations. Everything had to be checked thoroughly and, ideally, the system should have been set up so that it was impossible for anyone to make a mistake. As we found out, the smallest oversight could cause a major set-back."

Martin Broeders
Production Manager, Hollandia BV

Considerable effort had been made to tempt the media down to site to witness the uplift. A special press compound had been set up on Jubilee Gardens, with room for a dozen or more live-broadcast vehicles, and a viewing platform had been erected on The Queen's Walk close to the 'action'. Unfortunately, the final preparations on site took far longer than expected and it was several hours before action of any sort became apparent to those waiting on Jubilee Gardens or the Embankment opposite. Paul Baxter and Jamie Bowden tried their best to explain the delays to the assembled press *(above)*.

"The run-up to that first lift day was incredibly stressful. For about four weeks we had gone out of our way to court the press, both national and international, arranging visits to site and so on, getting them interested in covering 'the big day'. In the end, we had accreditation for around 200 organisations, with some 20 television stations broadcasting live for at least part of the day. Quite frankly, it was quite a surprise, as interest in the wheel before then had been quite low-key. It certainly raised the tension, and I spent quite a lot of time in the site office during that last week before the lift, trying to impress on people how important it was that everything went smoothly on the day. As I remember it, we finally received word that the lift was 'on' on the Thursday morning, just a day before the lift, although that particular date had been 'pencilled in' for some time. I was already camping out at the Marriott Hotel (in County Hall) by then, as we were working very long hours indeed during the last few days – making all the final arrangements, making sure everybody knew it was happening and so on. My one wish for the lift itself was that it would all pass off smoothly, so that we could just let everyone enjoy the show and have a nice easy day."

Jamie Bowden
Official Spokesman, British Airways London Eye

"I was in the bus we had set up as our on-site press office, talking to Paul Baxter when we heard the bang. That must have been at around 4.30pm. It had already been a long day, not least because we had originally told the press that the lift would begin at nine in the morning. When there had still been no movement by 2pm, they were understandably becoming restless, if not exactly hostile. Of course, Paul and I ran round to the viewing platform to see what was going on, still very much in the dark at that point as we had no idea if this was meant to happen or not. It quickly became apparent that something had gone wrong. From that point on, our main priority was to give out clear and accurate information to the media, preferably as soon as possible. There were three key questions: had anyone been hurt – and thankfully no one had; was the lift off – an emphatic yes; and when would it go ahead next – to which no one had an answer. I have been often asked since whether we had been right to have all the world's press on hand, when we could not be absolutely sure whether the lift would work, but I still think it was the correct decision. If nothing else, by bringing them in so close to the action, it helped them understand that this was no walk in the park. And, certainly, their reaction to the disappointment was far kinder than we could have dared hoped for."

Jamie Bowden
Official Spokesman, British Airways London Eye

A methodical sequence of operations had been established for the uplift – the load in the Mammoet strand-jacks *(left)* being increased in regular increments, with pauses at each stage to analyse the measurements being received from the sensors positioned all over the structure. All seemed to be going well, with the measurements corresponding almost exactly with the computer predictions. As one final step, it had been decided to deliberately overload the system by increasing the load in the strands to 110 per cent of that required to lift the wheel, actually raising the hub and spindle *(below)* while the rim was still held down on the support platforms. This increased the load on the auxiliary support cables spanning between the top of the spindle and the rim, and it was at this moment – with the media looking on – that one of them suddenly broke lose, the jolt causing the cables on either side to follow suit *(bottom left)*. The lift was stopped immediately.

"It's always the small things that catch you out. It is like that old nursery rhyme: for the want of a nail, the shoe was lost; for the want of a shoe, the horse was lost; for the want of a horse, the rider was lost; for the want of a rider, the battle was lost; and all for the want of a horse-shoe nail. In our case it was a bolt, but the principle is the same."

Allan Mann
Technical Director, Babtie Allott & Lomax

171

"Engineering is not just about the calculations; there is a practical element too. Good engineering, for example, should be insensitive to defects in workmanship – especially on site where one has to accept that particular operations cannot always be carried out exactly as planned. In that sense, of course, the failure during the first uplift was the result of poor engineering, but it would be wrong to say that it was any one person's fault. Mace and ourselves had recognised from the outset that with so much pressure on the project, mistakes were bound to sneak in. There was no point in trying to apportion blame – it was better by far that people be allowed to put all their energies into finding a solution. The curious thing was that in making it clear no one was to blame, everyone felt responsible. And so it was with the test. In a matter of days we were able to identify exactly what had happened and Hollandia had designed a possible solution – in fact, they had already machined an alternative fitting."

Allan Mann
Technical Director, Babtie Allott & Lomax

Working through the weekend, Hydrospex Cylap, the specialist contractor responsible for all the hydraulic lifting and tensioning equipment, built a test-rig in an attempt to duplicate the failure. It took a number of attempts, and then only by exaggerating the conditions. It had been noted that some of the brackets supporting the cable connections in question had not pulled straight as they came under tension, and it transpired that, under particular circumstances, the eccentric loading this misalignment imposed could force the connection's fixing collar out of line sufficiently to lose purchase on the bracket and allow the cable's fixing block to break lose. It was now a relatively simple task to redesign the collar and bracket to ensure the same sequence of events could not happen again.

There can be no deny-ing that the failure to achieve uplift at the first attempt came as a significant shock to all concerned. Para-doxically, the test had served its purpose and safely detected an un-expected weakness in the system. And, if nothing else, it had confirmed the stability of the main structure which had been en-tirely unaffected. The only embarrassment was that the one major set-back the project was to endure, in what had otherwise been a year of success, should have occurred in the full glare of media publicity. Sensibly, in-stead of rushing ahead, the decision was now made to step back and carefully reassess the situation and to see what else might be im-proved. The uplift was postponed a full month to allow everything to be checked thoroughly and the auxiliary sup-port cables and their connections to be re-placed *(right)*. At the same time, the proce-dures and schedules were reconfigured to allow other work to continue smoothly.

In the final days before the lift, the computer control and monitoring systems *(left)* were carefully calibrated and checked, as were all the necessary back-up systems and overrides.

"*The success of the uplift was based purely upon teamwork — and what a team it was. During that last week, Hollandia, Babtie Allott & Lomax, Iv-Infra, Tony Gee & Partners, Hydrospex, Mammoet and, of course, our own team from Mace were all on site, working together to close out the last of the outstanding engineering issues, all working very long hours with lots of inspections and lots of open discussion. And, in every instance, it was the very best people, the most senior designers and engineers. But there were no airs or graces. If an inspection had to be at four in the morning, they were there — striving to solve problems and guarantee the lift of the wheel; and not just looking to their own responsibilities, but helping each other out, always looking to achieve the common objective. And it was the same with the contractors. If further designs were needed, proposals were submitted, discussed, amended, agreed, installed and signed off — often all on the same day. Looking back, it is incredible just how much work was cleared in those last three or four days — and how much real confidence was gained. It was quite magical. Truly inspirational.*"

Neil Thompson
Design Manager, Mace Limited

Among those caught up in the last-minute discussions and checks were Tim Renwick, Allan Mann and John Roberts *(below)*; Nardo Hoogendijk and John Lovell *(centre)*; and Sytze Wierda of Iv-Infra *(bottom)*.

By early October, all the temporary cables had been replaced and the new fixing points at the rim checked. Other procedures had been improved and, at a final team meeting attended by all those directly involved in the lift *(opposite)*, it was confirmed that the revised uplift would now take place over the weekend of 9 and 10 October. As before, in the days leading up to the actual lift, the systems were method-ically checked and re-checked. At the same time, survey points — including one at the top of the Shell Build-ing *(bottom left)* — were set up from which the entire lift could be carefully monitored at all times. *Above*: Peter Koorevaar, Jacques Berenbak, Tjerko Jur-gens and Chiel Smits study the most recent weather forecast, con-firming good condi-tions during the lift weekend.

"The most telling moment in the lead-up to the second uplift was coming across a very relaxed Maarten Jongejan and his Dutch compatriots on the Friday afternoon, play-ing football in Jubilee Gardens against a team from Mace. I realised then that there was no way we were going to be in for the kind of day we had endured the month be-fore."

Jamie Bowden
Official Spokesman, British Airways London Eye

The lift was controlled via computers from a site office shared by Mammoet and Hydrospex *(below right)*, with all the relevant information relayed to a 'repeater' room in the Mace site office *(below left)* where it was monitored by the project's senior design engineers. By the evening of Friday 8 October, all the testing had been successfully completed, including a new overload test on the temporary cables. Everything was in place and the following morning, at around 9am, the wheel inched its way clear of the support platforms. As with all the pretesting, the lift itself was a gradual process during the early stages, with frequent stops to study the information from the monitoring equipment, adjust the stability cables fixed to the underside of the rim *(right)* and carry out regular surveys of the structure to ensure it was performing exactly as predicted.

"Our main concern was the stability of the overall system: it was essential the wheel remained straight at all times. We therefore introduced a system of cables, fixed to four points on the underside of the rim and connected back – via the support platforms in the river – to jacks fixed to the tension base, where the load in the cables could be constantly monitored and adjusted."

Nardo Hoogendijk
Design Engineer, Hollandia BV

"Meandering along the South Bank, as I do day after day on the way to work, I admire the London Eye. Its shocking scale, its bright-white simplicity, the huge effort to yank it up, the cheeky populism of placing something so essentially banal opposite the gouged and fissured pomp of the Palace of Westminster – all this is appealing. Perhaps, last week, it was at its best, hanging at a sickening angle over the river. There was a little splatter of boats and barges holding it on one side, and a web of metal wires in wisps and hanks, like a young girl's hair, on the other. The effect was a drawing from Gulliver's Travels. You cannot help but smile when you see it. I stood on a bright, cold, sunny morning watching the reaction on people's faces as they turned the corner of the Embankment and suddenly looked at this ridiculously big but familiar object, tilted there as if some monstrous dispatch rider in the sky, suspicious as all London cyclists are, had whipped off his front wheel to foil bike thieves, dumped it down and wandered off for a bacon sandwich the size of Parliament. Most grinned, some laughed. Whatever else it is, the London Eye this week has been very, very funny."

Andrew Marr
The Observer, 17 October 1999

The raising of British Airways London Eye to its upright – though not, at this stage, vertical – position took place over two days. During the first phase on Saturday, the structure was raised to 35 degrees *(below right)*, at which point it was 'locked off' for the night to allow the secondary stability cables, running between the underside of the rim and the temporary support platforms in the river, to be reconfigured. The uplift recommenced early on Sunday morning *(right)*, progressing steadily through the day and reaching its final position of 65 degrees, the permanent angle for the main A-frame legs, at around 5pm *(far right)*. Even at this incomplete stage, the top edge of the rim was some 110 metres above the river and was clearly visible from all over London. The next stage was to swing the rim itself out to the vertical, but this could only be achieved after a series of intermediate operations had been completed. These took several days and the wheel only reached its fully upright position a week later.

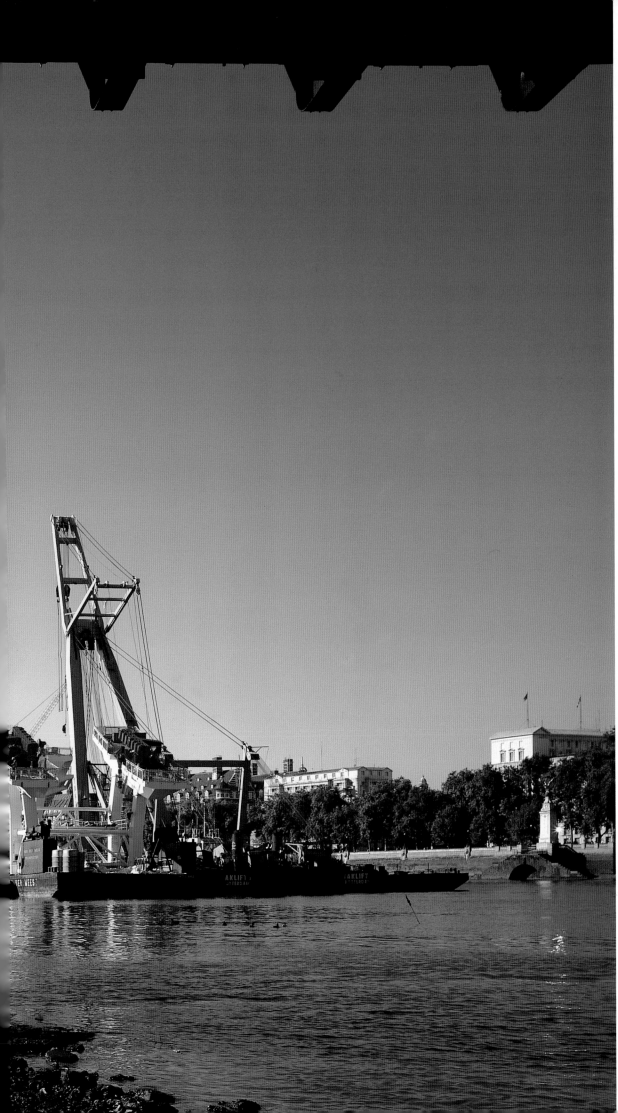

After the disappointment of the first uplift, publicity for the second attempt had been a little more guarded and press interest, certainly on the Saturday, was noticeably more low key. As the lift progressed, however, and reports started to appear on the news bulletins, more and more people began to arrive on the Embankment, Westminster Bridge and in Jubilee gardens to enjoy the show. It was, perhaps, at its most impressive early on Sunday morning, suspended out over the river at a seemingly impossible angle — as seen here (left) from the exposed shoreline below the Hungerford railway bridge. Note the all but completed restraint towers moored out in the river on barges alongside Taklift 3, waiting to be positioned under the rim in the following days while the wheel was held back at an angle of 65 degrees.

183

Measuring 110mm in diameter and weighing around 19 tonnes each, there are four backstays in total, all of which had been pin-jointed at the top of the A-frame before the uplift began. Drawn down into the tension chamber in part during the uplift, the operation was completed on Monday morning, taking great care not to damage the threaded end connectors as they were lowered through the steel anchor block *(right)*. Once in place, the permanent hydraulic jacks set on to the back of the anchor block *(above)* gradually increased the tension in the cables to their full working load of around 550 tonnes, at which point the cables were 'locked off' by tightening threaded collars previously fitted over their end connectors. With a breaking load for each cable in excess of 1100 tonnes, the entire wheel can be safely supported by two cables alone.

Following a full survey to confirm the wheel's A-frame legs were held securely at the correct angle *(below)*, the support of the entire structure was transferred from the Mammoe strand-jacks to the permanent back-stay cables.

Both the main drive and the lateral stability systems are mounted on heavy pin-jointed frames, with powerful hydraulic rams that allow the different elements to be fully withdrawn for maintenance purposes.

"Hollandia approached Croese in November 1998, quite early in the design phase, to advise on drive mechanisms and anchorage devices for the wheel. We had worked with them before, so they knew of our experience designing drive systems for mobile cranes, transport systems and the like. We have even worked on other types of rides, including roller-coasters and carousels, so it was fairly easy to come up with a basic design strategy – the hard work, as always, was in resolving the details. The key concern from the outset was to design a system with a guaranteed level of reliability, which is best achieved using a known technology run well within its limits. The obvious solution in this case, therefore, was to apply the drive at the rim using standard lorry tyres turned by hydraulic motors. These are very quiet and, more importantly, they allow the drive load to be balanced across any number of wheels with ease, even when some are turning at slightly different speeds – an important requirement here as the rim is actually slightly faceted. Because the overall structure of the wheel is balanced, the drive loads are, in fact, relatively low, mainly counteracting friction and wind loadings and, of course, the eccentric loading caused by different numbers of people in the capsules – actually worst in the morning or evening when the wheel opens and closes."

Wim Huis In't Veld
Design Engineer, Nelcon BV
formerly of Croese Engineering Consultants BV

The wheel's design calls for two large restraint towers positioned at each end of the boarding platform. One of these accommodates the main drive system, while both provide lateral support against wind loading and help guide the capsules past the boarding and alighting areas. Each tower takes the form of a pair of working platforms — between which the rim passes — raised high above the river on a heavily braced rectangular frame. The platforms follow the curve of the rim and rise at a distinct angle in their final positions, but were laid horizontally in the Hollandia yard *(opposite)* for greater convenience during the installation of the stability and drive systems. Transferred to London in time for the first uplift — on the assumption that the final fit-out and commissioning would be undertaken once in place on site — the delay allowed work to be completed in advance *(above)*, while the restraint towers were moored out in the river.

"Engineering for safety can be a difficult topic — one that many people aren't entirely used to — but it is something we had to think about very carefully. We had to consider, for example, how people might be evacuated from the wheel. It is clearly far better if this can be avoided entirely, and one of our main priorities, therefore, was to ensure the wheel can be turned at all times."

Allan Mann
Technical Director, Babtie Allott & Lomax

"Hydraudyne was responsible for the installation of the main drive systems, the guiding roller 'sets' that provide lateral stability, and all the necessary control and monitoring systems. As conceived by Croese, the drive system is actually made up of four separate drive units, two on each side of the rim, each with four drive wheels operating in pairs that grip continuous 'running beams' fixed along each side of the rim's outer frame. In normal operation, all 16 wheels will run in unison, but the system has been designed with sufficient capacity to allow individual pairs of wheels to be retracted, should a problem occur, with no effect on the running speed. The wheel can be run normally with only 12 wheels in operation and can be safely evacuated with as few as eight, though turning at a slightly lower speed. The running beam has a high-grip coating and each pair of wheels is fitted with sensors that increase the drive pressure automatically should any slippage be detected. It is a fairly standard system and is considered very reliable. Even so, we have built in a high level of redundancy that should guarantee near-permanent operation. There are two separate hydraulic supply lines, for example, and each drive unit can be isolated and run independently – off a separate compressor if necessary. And as a final back-up, should all hydraulic pressure be lost, electric motors and mechanical brakes have been installed within the hub of each wheel. By Hydraudyne standards, this really is quite a small system, and the

Though not entirely stable in this position, the rim was held back against the A-frame legs in the week following the uplift to allow unimpeded access to the boarding platform and its immediate surroundings. This greatly simplified the lifting into place of the last of the major elements: the prefabricated control and electrical rooms on the boarding platform and, more importantly, the two main restraint towers. It was imperative, however, that these operations be completed as quickly as possible. The restraint towers were lifted into place on successive days by Taklift 3 which, like its larger brother Taklift 1, had been sailed over from The Netherlands specially for this project. The towers were lifted in as finished units, with both of their respective working platforms — known, because of their curved form, as bananas — in place. Only when the towers were securely bolted down on to their blue base frames, which had been fixed securely to their respective foundation piles prior to the uplift, were the landside 'bananas' lifted clear to provide clearance for the rim as it was swung into the vertical position.

real complexity of the job — apart from controlling the logistics of such a short design and installation programme — was actually the design of the control and monitoring systems. Safety for the passengers and the operating staff was paramount, so it was essential that the systems were as simple to use and understand as possible, while foolproof protocols were also built in to ensure dangerous operations were not possible. It wasn't exactly helpful when the uplift was delayed and we had to complete the work out in the river, where access and power were limited. Still, we were determined that we would not be the ones to let the project down. If anything, it became a matter of honour that we complete the work on time, so it was very pleasing to have the systems ready to run just days after the swing to vertical had been completed."

Bart Wiegmans
Project Manager, Hydraudyne Systems & Engineering BV

Capable of lifting loads in excess of 200 tonnes at an outreach of 20 metres, Taklift 3 — though significantly smaller than Taklift 1 — remained an impressive sight and was guaranteed to draw large crowds of spectators, particularly when manoeuvring the restraint towers close in to the river wall *(below left)*. As with all the structural steelwork, careful setting out during fabrication and assembly ensured the restraint towers, complete with their pin-jointed diagonal bracing, fitted on to their respective bases perfectly at first attempt *(right)*.

"For the past 10 days a festival has been going on on the banks of the Thames. People are stopping, gawping, pointing, snapping their compact cameras and setting up their long-lensed ones on tripods, swapping newly minted urban myths and, above all, grinning in spontaneous expressions of pleasure. After decades of architects and politicians blathering about bringing life back to the river, it has actually happened. The thing they are grinning at is the raising of 'The Wheel' . . . In this year of grand circular phenomena, the raising gives the most simple and direct satisfaction, less anticlimactic than the eclipse, more spontaneous than the Dome. It is a true people's monument, to use an idea that needs rescuing from the clutches of Tony Blair's wordsmiths. The wheel is a big toy, something graspable and instantly comprehensible, whose lifting into place is an action of childlike simplicity. The addictive thrills of building, of flirting with disaster before eventual triumph, which are usually known only to the consenting adults of the construction industry and hidden behind hoardings, have here been shared by everyone. The fact that the first attempt to raise it failed and that it has been teetering at a frightening angle for this past week have all been part of the drama."

Rowan Moore
The Evening Standard, 18 October 1999

"The most demanding job for Taklift 3 was replacing one of the working platforms. This had been removed easily enough when its re-straint tower was first positioned (left), but once the rim was vertical it could only be lifted back by slipping Taklift 3's flying jib between the spoke cables. A couple of these were moved to one side, but the manoeuvre still demanded absolute precision."

Jan Kwadijk
Project Manager, Takmarine BV

By the evening of Wednesday 13 October *(left)*, just three days after the first phase of the uplift had been completed, British Airways London Eye was supported on its own backstay cables and the two restraint towers had been lowered into place. Its work complete, the Mammoet A-frame, which had stood guard over the site for the past five weeks, was being lowered using the same cables that had previously lifted the wheel. By Friday it was again lying on its temporary supports running nearly the full length of the site, and its cables had been disconnected. Within a week it had been broken down into its container-size travelling components and sent on its way. With the final preparations now completed, including the realignment of the stability cables, all was ready to swing the rim to vertical.

The swing to vertical was achieved using the four permanent stay cables that run from the end of the spindle down to fixing brackets welded to the bottom of the A-frame legs. It was a delicate operation, not least because the threaded connections at the end of the stays had to be carefully aligned and slotted into their respective brackets while in full tension. Starting at 9 o'clock on the Saturday morning, the entire operation was to take more than 18 hours, the rim finally reaching the vertical position (opposite) in the very early hours of Sunday 17 October.

In the week between the uplift and the swing to vertical, the wheel was visited by a number of celebrities, including Richard Rogers and Frank Dobson (above right, top and bottom), as well as Bob White, chairman of Mace (far right, opposite). As ever, Jamie Bowden (right) was on hand during the critical phases of the operation to explain what was going on to the media and passers-by alike.

"The swing out to vertical was actually far harder than the uplift. With the uplift, there were just the four Mammoet strand-jacks working together to do the actual lifting and another four jacks to let out the stability cables – just two systems, each working in a more-or-less linear arrangement that could be controlled automatically. With the swing to vertical, however, the strand-jacks operating the stability cables connected to the top and bottom of the rim now worked in opposite directions and not in a linear fashion, while the lift itself was controlled through a further eight strand-jacks which had to be operated very precisely in pairs. Now, we had three separate systems to worry about, each with its own operator. And because of the way the sets of cables worked against each other, all the adjustments had to be made very gradually. Even the two jacks pulling on each backstay had to be adjusted independently – to ensure the long end connectors were perfectly aligned with their respective fixing brackets. And then, of course, we had some burglars who made the mistake of trying to get on to one of the barges while we were all on site – the work had to be stopped until the police had taken them away. It ended up being a very long day."

Tjerko Jurgens
Managing Director, Hydrospex Cylap BV

By the beginning of November, British Airways London Eye was firmly established as a major new landmark on the city's skyline, as this panoramic photograph *(main spread)* taken from the roof of Millbank Tower shows. The London Eye is the capital's fourth highest structure — after the old NatWest and Post Office Towers and Canary Wharf — and can be seen from all over London, with clear vantage points as far distant as Hampstead Heath in the north and Richmond Park to the south-west. With the wheel held firmly in the vertical position, work had commenced immediately on commissioning the main drive systems *(left)*. All went smoothly and the rim made its first tentative revolutions during the last days of October, clearing the way for the arrival of the first capsules on site on Saturday 6 November.

"I have known David and Julia for years, but we hadn't really spoken about the wheel until we met up by chance at a design show in London in October 1996. We talked about the work I was doing, the yachts and so on, and the 'Airstream' caravan I had recently redesigned. Anyway, something must have clicked, because a month or so later they asked me to help out with the design of the capsules. The general principles of the design – the ring supports, the American football shape, even the overall dimensions –

had been fixed during the competition stage. My role, therefore, concentrated more on how the capsules might be built – identifying the most appropriate materials, exploring how the overall proportions might be adjusted to simplify fabrication, that sort of thing – but all the while respecting David and Julia's initial vision and trying to maintain the purity of the overall shape. Arup's had done some work on the mechanical systems and sketched out a basic structure but, even so, many of the practical issues were still

open to discussion. We quickly reached the stage where it was sensible to seek further input from industry, from those companies that might actually manufacture the capsules, and we approached a number of companies we thought might be able to help – from boat builders and car makers to the manufacturers of railway carriages and monorail systems."

Nic Bailey
Design Consultant

From the outset, David Marks and Julia Barfield were determined that the capsules should combine unprecedented stability with the best possible views. Instead of the top-hung passenger cabins of traditional observational wheels, therefore, with their tendency to sway and support frames that obscure the view, they proposed that their capsules should be fully supported in two rings, promoting uninterrupted views in every direction, and fitted with an active drive mechanism to keep the floor level at all times. Early studies — explored through a series of freehand sketches (left) — show a basic concept that has remained virtually unchanged. Even the overall dimensions are the same, although at this stage it was assumed that all passengers would be seated. Though Arup's made a series of practical studies, it was not until planning was approved in April 1996 that the design of the capsules accelerated significantly, most notably with the addition to the team, in November of that year, of freelance designer Nic Bailey. With the skilled use of computer graphics — including the drawings of the final design shown here (far left and below) — Nic was able to refine the basic concept to the point where the Poma Group of France, working through its subsidiary Sigma SA, was able to produce an accurate mock-up (bottom left) in late 1997.

"I have been working with the Poma Group on an ad hoc *basis for the past 17 years, ever since they installed one of their cable cars at my own theme park here in Derbyshire. I had seen the reports about the London Eye project in the trade press and realised that Poma's experience in the design and fabrication of both cable-car and monorail systems might be of relevance, and I contacted David (Marks) and Julia (Barfield) to offer our services. It turned out they had already spent some months looking for companies they could work with to develop the concept. I organised a trip down to the south of France for David and Nic Bailey, where they met Jean-Paul Cathiard, the President of the Poma Group, and saw the factories there and examples of the company's work. They must have been impressed because, soon after, we were commissioned to make the full-size mock-up."*

Andrew Pugh
Managing Director, The Heights of Abraham

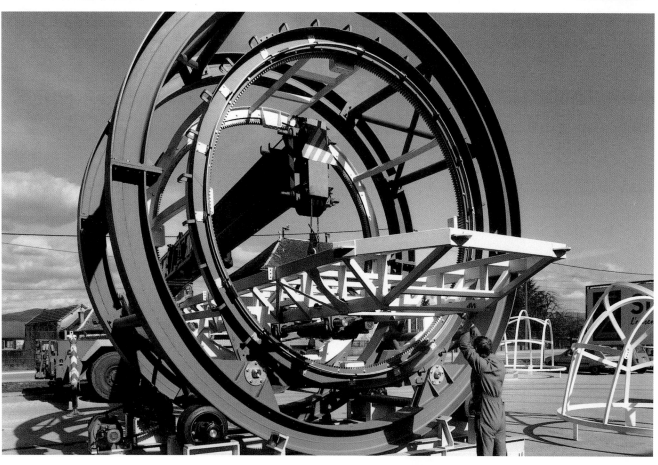

"We are approached once or twice a year by people asking for advice on various crazy projects and, to be honest, our first impression was that this was probably just another of those – so we didn't take it very seriously to begin with."

Philippe Desflammes
Project Manager, Sigma SA

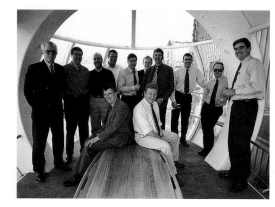

In September 1998, the Poma Group and its subsidiary Sigma SA were formally appointed to undertake the detail design and fabrication of the 32 capsules, to be supplied to site complete in every detail.

Working together with Semer SA, a sister company in the Poma Group with extensive experience in the design and production of complex electronic operating systems for all types of cable car, Sigma decided to build a full-scale test-rig in which their proposed solution could be thoroughly assessed. Completed in February 1999, it was to become an ideal test-bed for a wide variety of design ideas and was visited regularly over the following months by different members of the project team, travelling either independently or as part of the overall steering group. The photographs shown here, including the group portrait taken in the mock-up *(opposite page, bottom)*, were taken during an early visit in March 1999.

"Sigma was established in 1964, as a specialist in the design and fabrication of cable-car gondolas, and acted as a strategic supplier to Poma for many years before becoming part of the group in the 1980s. Up until the early 1990s, nearly all our work was for the ski-lift market, but we have diversified in recent years, such that nowadays around 30 per cent of our business falls into other categories. The work on the wheel was, therefore, part of a logical progression for us. The design was still evolving when we first became involved and everyone seemed to have an opinion. We were receiving instructions from David, from Nic and from Arup's, as well having meetings with Paul Baxter from British Airways, which was not always easy. The real breakthrough came with the making of the mock-up — suddenly, everyone could grasp exactly what the capsule would be like; what it would look like; what it would feel like inside. It also helped resolve a number of key issues. We studied the proposed loading procedures, for example, by pulling the mock-up past a raised platform at various speeds to see how many people could get on or off in set distances. Interestingly, the tests showed that most people preferred to stand and move around inside the capsule, allowing the fixed seats to be removed and the capacity of the capsule to be comfortably increased from 16 to 25."

Jean-Francois Savard
Project Director, Sigma SA

The design of the test-rig was a major undertaking in its own right. Sigma had to find a way of turning the capsule's external fixing points around the full diameter of the capsule, in such a way that simulated exactly the movement of a capsule around the finished wheel. After careful consideration, this was achieved by fixing the capsule to the inside of two large braced rings, supported on rollers. These external rings could then be rotated at the appropriate speed by an independent electric motor, while the drive mechanism in the capsule kept the capsule itself level. In its final form, the drive mechanism — which together with all its control and monitoring devices is now known as the stability system — has to respond to two basic conditions: it must synchronise the speed of each capsule's rotation to match exactly the turning of the rim, gauging its position on the wheel and holding the floor perfectly level, while at the same time responding to the changing loads imposed on the floor due to the movement of the passengers. In Semer's solution, the turning speed of the drive mechanism is constantly adjusted by a series of finely calibrated inclinometers, which are able to restrict the movement of the floor to less than 0.1 of a degree.

"One of our major concerns was just how it would feel inside the capsules, particularly in a strong wind. Everything in our experience told us it must move in some way, but no one could tell us how much. I remember several surreal conversations, trying to get a clear indication of what a trip in a capsule might feel like. Parallels were made with ships at sea, but were these big ships or were they more like rowing boats? Was the sea calm or was it choppy, or was there just a big swell? It was clear we could run the wheel in high winds, but would people accept it — would they feel safe?"

Andrew Potter
General Manager, The Tussaud's Group

206

"In essence, when we were approached again in September 1998, we had to start from scratch. Just how the mounting rings and big bearings might work had been discussed, of course, during the making of the mock-up, and we had some ideas for the main structure, but no calculations had ever been made. We had even had some trial pieces of glass made, by a Swiss company, to see what we might learn about double-curved glass, but these only demonstrated how difficult it would be. Even so, we were fairly

confident we could make our basic concept work. Our main concern was the stability system. Keeping the floor level was not a problem if the loads were evenly balanced, but we had no idea how the system would react as people moved around. Would you feel any movement? If so, would it be acceptable, or was it better to remove all sensation of movement entirely? We couldn't be sure and it soon became clear that most of these issues could only be resolved using a full-scale test-rig. Unfortunately, there was

very little time. Many of the components — the main ring bearings, for example — had to be ordered well in advance, so we ended up making the test-rig with the real pieces as they became available, which was not ideal. Subsequent changes might be possible to some elements, but not to others. It was a huge relief, therefore, when the stability system worked perfectly from its first run."

Philippe Desflammes
Project Manager, Sigma SA

"Curiously, the overall dimensions of the capsules have not changed that much. We did look at what savings might be made if the capsules were smaller, but they turned out to be quite minor. You saved on materials, but the number of joints remained the same and, if anything, the overall complexity only increased, as it became ever more difficult to fit all the equipment in."

Nic Bailey
Design Consultant

The expense of complex tooling could not be justified for 32 capsules alone and, during the early stages, much of the basic structural frame was made by hand, the work being undertaken by skilled welders at the Sacmi factory, a sister company of Sigma in the Poma Group. As with the rim, though on a far smaller scale, the separate elements — including the floor *(below)* and the curved glazing frames that form each end of the capsule *(left)* — were formed in pre-cut and, in the case of the latter, pre-curved steel sections assembled on master jigs. With the rapid heating and cooling caused by the welding process distorting the metal slightly on each occasion, a strict sequence had to be maintained to ensure subsequent welds 'balanced' each other out.

"From the outset, the real problem was always going to be meeting the delivery dates. There was very little time to spare, so it was important everything ran smoothly. There was a great deal of pressure to complete the design and confirm the calculations as soon as possible, so that orders could be placed in good time. Due to the nature of our work, we rely on subcontractors a great deal and we had to work to their schedules. Fortunately, we developed a very good relationship with Allott & Lomax, which allowed decisions to be agreed quickly. We could keep everything moving forward, but this only emphasised that there was no time to change your mind, let alone start again. There was always the slight doubt that maybe there was a better solution. Fortunately, we knew the mechanical systems we had worked very well and there was no need to change them. This was not always the case, however, with those issues affecting the 'look' of the capsule. David and Nic had a specific vision, a particular feeling for what the capsules should be like. It was our responsibility to turn that dream into reality — into actual shop drawings, calculations and materials — but finding a solution that everyone was happy with could be very difficult, and on many occasions the schedule was stretched to the absolute limit."

Jean-Francois Savard
Project Director, Sigma SA

With insufficient space within its own factory to build 32 capsules, Sigma decided to rent and recommission a vacant factory in Grenoble which was almost purpose-made for the job. Full-height access at each end of the long space, which came complete with travelling cranes in the roof, allowed a clear production line to be established, with individual components arriving at one end and finished capsules leaving at the other. Taken over in late April 1999, the assembly of the first 12 capsules was well under way by the time these photographs were taken in mid-June. The basic structural components could hardly have been simpler. First came the fully braced floor frame into which was installed, at this stage, only the drive mechanism for the stability system *(below)*. Once this had been completed, the floor was then inserted into what is effectively the capsule's chassis: a central structural 'drum' that supports, at each end, the four-metre diameter ring bearings *(right)*. The floor frame, the central drum and the end glazing frames are all supported on the 'internal' side of each bearing, while the 'external' side incorporates the pin-joint connections that will attach the capsule to the rim. A toothed rail fixed to the 'external' side of the bearing provides the purchase against which the cogs of the capsule's drive mechanism can turn, and thus maintain the floor at horizontal.

All of the capsules' operating systems — including the lighting air conditioning, public address, radio links and emergency sensors, as well as all the controls and monitors for the stability system — were developed by Semer at their factory near Le Fayet, at the foot of Mont Blanc, and installed by them during the capsules' assembly in Grenoble. To ensure the systems run smoothly and without interruption at all times, each capsule is fitted with duplicate control boxes, located at each end of the floor space, one acting as a permanent back-up to the other. Both boxes can draw power from one of two separate power supplies, while back-up batteries hold sufficient power to run essential services for up to three hours in the event of an unexpected power cut.

"There is an awful lot of mechanical equipment in the floor and we spent a great deal of time trying to find the best way to fit it all in. We didn't want bulges appearing in the external skin, but at the same time we didn't want the floor rising too high into the capsule and reducing the sense of spaciousness that both David and I always saw as an essential part of the ride's overall quality."

Nic Bailey
Design Consultant

"Semer have a long experience of designing automatic control systems for all sorts of industrial and public transport systems, from quarries and steelworks to automatic monorails systems and every type of cable-car operation. All of these applications are safety critical in one way or another, so we are used to designing our systems to very strict specifications and with high degrees of redundancy. We have to consider the hardware, of course, and make sure it will operate reliably under the expected conditions, but more importantly we must develop good software – compatible with the hardware and easy to use, both in operating and monitoring mode. The biggest danger in any complex system is the operator misunderstanding the information. To ensure the best possible standards, we have developed our own quality plan, running two software design teams against each other, one to design the system and the other to test it, to expose its flaws. Improvements are made, then tested again until we can be sure any bugs have been removed. Much of this comes down to instilling a culture of safety in the workforce. In fact, a high proportion of our people come from the aeronautic or transport industries, where safety is already a priority. After that it is a matter of checking and testing at every stage: in the laboratory, in the factory and finally, of course, on site."

Marc Bottollier
Project Manager, Semer SA

"On a project of this scale and complexity you are always looking for a safe pair of hands. This was especially the case with the glass – I must have spent around three months chasing around Europe trying to identify the right manufacturer. Finding the quality we required at a reasonable price proved to be a major challenge. In the end, we invited three companies to prepare samples for us – one from Britain, one from Spain and, of course, Sunglass from Italy.

Quite frankly, there was no competition and Sunglass got the job. I undertook a number of these company reviews for all sorts of components, and it was always an eye-opening experience. With such a high profile it was hardly surprising that the project was attractive to many companies. What was odd was that they all seemed to have an opinion – even when, as was often the case, it soon became clear they had no idea what the job actually entailed. There were occasions when you could only assume

somebody must be having you on. It was such a relief to come across companies that had an immediate grasp of the technical and programming difficulties, and could offer sensible solutions."

Neil Thompson
Design Manager, Mace Limited

The capsule glazing had to be manufactured to very exacting standards to maintain both the perfectly smooth shape the designers had in mind and the highest optical quality — not always easy when every panel is curved in both directions, in the case of the main end panels to a degree that had never previously been attempted. The Italian manufacturer Sunglass s.r.l. was identified as one of the few companies capable of completing the job to the quality required, and the work was carried out at its factory near Padua. For the simpler glass panels, two layers of 6mm-thick glass — precut to the correct size — were placed in specially produced moulds into which the glass 'fell' as it was heated. The two layers were moulded at the same time to ensure a perfect 'fit' during the lamination process. For the more demanding end panels, with their very deep curvatures, Sunglass developed and refined their own techniques to ensure every panel was produced to the requisite quality.

As each glass panel was completed, it was checked on a specially fabricated jig *(left)* to ensure it matched the required shape exactly.

"Glass technology has improved dramatically in recent years. There have been many developments in the car industry, for example, but the shapes still tend to be quite simple. Curves are either relatively shallow or are more acute in one direction only. It soon became clear that we needed to find a company willing to work well beyond the usual standards."

Nic Bailey
Design Consultant

215

The lamination process began with the thorough cleaning of the two glass sheets that make up an individual panel *(right)*, after which 1.5mm of lamination film, in one or two layers depending on requirements, was stretched between them and taped into place *(far right)*. The completed 'sandwich' was then sealed in a vacuum bag *(opposite)* and carefully stacked on a purpose-designed trolley, ready for transferring to an autoclave. Here, the panels were reheated under vacuum, following a very precise heating and cooling programme, causing the lamination film — opaque in its initial form — to clear and bond completely with the adjacent glass surfaces. Absolute precision was essential as the slightest flaw can cause the panel to crack.

"Sigma first contacted us in mid-September 1998, though at that time this was only to see if we were interested in the project and to check if we thought it was actually possible. There were many technical complications, but we liked the challenge and that led to us being asked — in competition with two other companies — to make up some test panels. The tolerances were very tight indeed. Because of the way the glass is fitted, without external frames, the individual panels had to be cut to size with great accuracy and shaped precisely. With 36 panels of glass making up just one capsule, this was already a significant challenge. And because of the capsule's elliptical floor-plan, the curves are not always constant. It turned out that there were seven distinct shapes for bending, six of which worked in symmetry — requiring 13 moulds in all. The real challenge however, was maintaining a high optical quality in the two main end panels. As a rule of thumb, we normally

Sunglass provides a complete service, including its own lamination process which is carried out in a dedicated 'clean' room, fitted with its own climate control to ensure optimum, dust-free working conditions at all times.

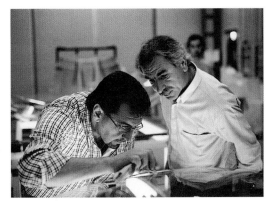

work to a maximum camber of around one in eight – that is, the height of the curve above the plane formed by the panel's sides is never more than one-eighth the length of the shortest side. Here, we were being asked to produce panels of glass with cambers of up to one in four – and not just single sheets, but always two sheets perfectly matched for lamination, which requires that the touching surfaces are exactly parallel. There was a lot of research – different types of glass, various temperature gradients and so on – and we made at least a dozen prototypes, recording and analysing the results at every stage, before we achieved the required quality. The final challenge, after that, was to achieve the same results in all 1152 panels."

Giuseppe Bergamin
Managing Director, Sunglass s.r.l.

Weighing anything up to 80 kilos each, the 36 glass panels that make up the glazing for one capsule had to be fitted with extreme precision to ensure the seamlessly smooth form specified by the design. The upper panels were positioned first with the help of a hydraulic lifting bracket *(below)*, being carefully aligned on the white-painted steel frame with the use of shims and spacers in the form of continuous strips and blocks. Once their final position had been approved, the panels were then fixed in place with black silicon sealant, applied in two phases: the main fixing layer first, injected internally between the glass surface and the steel frame *(below left)*, followed by the weather seal, injected externally between the panels. A back-up mechanical fixing is also provided, in the form of a stainless steel disc, fixed back to the steel frame at the point where the corners of four panels come together. Unsurprisingly, it did not take long for someone to notice that the complex ellipsoidal shape of the end glazing frames bore a remarkable similarity to old-fashioned 'pen-tops'. The name caught on and was used thereafter, in France as well as the UK.

"We did look at the possibility of using tinted or mirror-coated glass for the direct vision panels – the roof glazing is coated slightly – but I always felt that clear glass was the right option in thermal engineering terms. This is because the application of any form of treatment causes the glass to get hot when exposed to the sun and, in my experience, this heat is radiated into the interior in a way that is more uncomfortable than the heat of sunlight felt through clear glass. Furthermore, clear glass also allows much of the incident solar energy to pass right through the capsule. This goes rather against conventional wisdom, but I firmly believe that, in this particular application, it is appropriate. Provided the capsule air temperature is kept at the right level, passengers can now move around freely – in and out of the sun – until they find the balance that suits them best."

Loren Butt
Director, Loren Butt Consultancies

219

The internal lighting, loudspeakers, security cameras and sensors are all located behind a suspended panel in the ceiling *(right)*, which can be dropped down to allow access either for maintenance or to an emergency access hatch in the roof.

"One of the great benefits of having all 32 capsules under the same roof, and at different stages of construction, was that we could adapt very quickly to any necessary changes in the programme – when particular components didn't arrive on time, for example – allowing us to use the time available to the best possible advantage."

Andrew Pugh
Managing Director, The Heights of Abraham

The fit-out of all 32 capsules was a long and complex procedure, completed in just over five months between late April and early October 1999. For the most part, they were prepared in sets of four or six, in recognition of the weekly transport schedules that came into effect when the first capsules — complete in every detail except for the central wooden bench — left the Grenoble factory at the beginning of September

(above). Working upwards, the fit-out of the systems within the floor frame was completed first, followed by the fitting of the floor panels. With the floor in place, the fixing of the final wiring around the central drum and behind the ceiling panel could be completed with relative ease. The glazing came next, after which all that remained was the fixing, both internally and externally, of the fibre-glass cover panels and the doors.

"I have been involved with the wheel, on and off, since the competition stage, advising on ways that it might be powered from the ebb tidal flow of the river. Then, during the early design development phase, I worked alongside Arup's and Nic Bailey looking into how the capsules might be air-conditioned. This is when we started using the advanced techniques of fluid dynamics analysis to study the thermal environment, techniques that were to play a vital part as the design progressed. Everything changed again in October 1998, when the design team realised there was a need for someone to provide a co-ordinated overview of all the mechanical and electrical services used on the project. It was a daunting prospect which involved travelling all over Europe to gain a clear understanding of all the systems involved. I can't claim to be an expert in all of these, but I was able to develop a good grasp of the general principles which allowed me to concentrate on my prime task of developing the correct conceptual approach. I did, however,

maintain a particular interest in the capsule air conditioning. To all intents and purposes, the capsules are complete little buildings, encompassing nearly every fundamental issue ever encountered by an environmental engineer — from large numbers of people in a small space and very high solar heat gains to the problems of condensation and unusual methods of air distribution."

Loren Butt
Managing Director, Loren Butt Consultancies

With time at a premium, fabrication of the capsules continued through the weekends and late into the evenings on most nights, the evenings in particular proving a good time to carry out the sensitive electronic tests that had to be completed on each of the capsules' extensive operating and monitoring systems before it could be signed off as complete.

As well as the usual operating systems for the air-conditioning units, security sensors, the stability system and the like, all relatively familiar in their own way, Semer was also appointed to undertake the installation of the internal lighting and public address systems. Both were expected to perform to the highest possible standards, a specification which involved a level of subjective appreciation far removed from the company's usual operations. The lighting design, in particular, involves a very subtle balancing of different light sources to allow the internal lighting at night to shift seamlessly from pure white, during embarkation and disembarkation, to dark blue as the capsules rise — so as to reduce the internal reflections from the glass and improve the night time views. Semer found there was only so much they could achieve in their own workshops and laboratories, and much of the final fine-tuning was completed in the actual capsules, most often during the quiet of the evening or, with the lighting *(left and below)*, in the dark of night.

"As a designer, it is all too easy to become over-concerned by the quality of the finishes, to look in minute detail at every element, pointing out defects that most people will never see. The problem is, if there is too much of that sort of thing, it soon adds up to the point where people will notice, even if only subconsciously. It takes the edge off the overall experience in some way."

Nic Bailey
Design Consultant and Naval Architect

By early September — as shown by the photographs included here — the first capsules were nearing completion and the final checks and inspections were well in hand. This is never the easiest moment on any project and it was no help here that many of the opinions — regarding the quality of the finishes, for example — were to some extent subjective. Aware of the difficulties of carrying out remedial work once the capsules were in place on the wheel, Mace was particularly concerned that as much of the work, including any corrections, was completed before the capsules left Grenoble. It was, inevitably, a time for compromise, when passions could run high.

"One of the hardest things for us to take on board was the realisation that there was no comparison between the capsules and a standard gondola. We had to eliminate a whole way of thinking. The primary purpose of the typical gondola is to move the maximum number of people in the shortest possible time. Skiers do not normally worry about the view and they do not expect high standards of comfort; no heating is required and lighting is normally minimal. In normal operations, a ski-lift is little more than a Metro system in the air. With the capsules, on the other hand, the quality of the ride, the comfort of the passengers, is everything. Sudden or unexpected movements must be eliminated; there has to be heating and cooling available at all times, and the best possible finishes are expected. A gondola of this size would probably carry more than 100 people, but would weigh no more than 1.5 tonnes when empty. The glass used in a single capsule weighs that amount on its own, while the stability system adds a further tonne if the bearings are included — and all this, of course, requires a heavier and stronger structure to hold it in place. It is hardly surprising, therefore, that a capsule designed to carry 25 adults has ended up weighing around 10 tonnes."

Philippe Desflammes
Project Manager, Sigma SA

It had been understood since the competition stage that the capsules, wherever they were made, would have to make part of their journey to site by road and this, in part, determined that their overall diameter was fixed at around 4 metres — well within the maximum width allowed to travel on public roads without a full police escort. What this calculation failed to take into account, however, was that at this diameter, even when loaded on the lowest flatbed trailer, the finished capsules would stand some 4.8 metres high. This is fine in the UK, where most motorway bridges have a clear headroom of 5 metres or more, but was not a great help in France where some bridges across the autoroutes have been designed with allowable headrooms as low as 4.3 metres. There was no alternative but to find a route from Grenoble to Zeebrugge that avoided all low bridges. During the seven-week transport period that followed, villages the length of France became used to the sight of yet another 'convoi exceptionnel' passing through their midsts (below and far right), as the capsules made their long journey to the English Channel — and from there to a secure holding area near Dartford Bridge (below right and bottom).

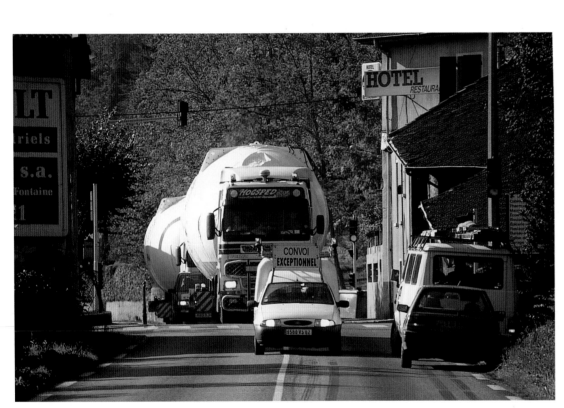

"We were first approached by Sigma some time in March 1999. We had not worked with them before, but as one of Europe's leading specialists in the transport of oversized or delicate loads, it was not that unusual to be approached by a French company. I must say they had an interesting problem for us. At around 10 tonnes, the capsules weigh considerably less than a standard container, so the weight was not an issue. There is a lot of glass, of course, which is always a concern, but the real problem here was always going to be the overall dimensions. At four metres wide, a full police escort would not be required — although they did prove necessary at certain localised points — but there were all sorts of other arrangements to be made. Permits had to be approved; English and French pilot cars and their crews had to be hired; appropriate ferries had to be booked; and, most importantly of all, a route had to be found that avoided all obstacles. And the key obstacles in France, we knew from experience, would be the fixed road bridges which are generally very low. We knew Zeebrugge in Belgium would be the destination, as that is one of only two ports operating ferries large enough. The trick was sorting out what happened in the 500 miles in between. A certain amount could be achieved with maps, but at a certain point there was no alternative but to travel the route by car. Every thoroughfare and junction had to be considered, starting with the decision to turn left or right out of the factory. With that out of the way, it was a question of logistics, with every town and locality having to be approached to see what permissions might be required, and not just once but for 16 separate convoys, each of two capsules, travelling at three or four day intervals over a seven-week period. After all that, the transfer in England to the holding point at Dartford was relatively straightforward."

Peter Dafters
Managing Director, Peter Dafters (STG) Ltd

227

To facilitate the lifting of the capsules, a purpose-made platform and mobile lifting rig — designed by Sigma, fabricated by Hollandia and installed by Tilbury Douglas — was positioned directly under the wheel at the same level as the boarding platform. This projected out into the river sufficiently to allow one capsule at a time to be lifted directly from one of two barges — specially converted and operated by Peter Dafters (STG) Ltd to transport all the capsules upriver from Dartford — into the mobile lifting rig (left). The rig was then pull-ed back into position below the rim and aligned with the support frame above. Four hydraulic jacks — one at each corner — were then able to gently raise each of the capsules into place, the jacks operating independently to allow the pin-joints to be aligned precisely. To maximise use of the lifting rig, the long, tubular tuned-mass-dampers used to reduce vibrations in the rim — seen left, already in place on the rig's highest platforms — were fitted to the rim at the same time, one on each side of every capsule.

Under pressure to make up the time lost during the delayed up-lift, the fitting of the capsules proceeded very quickly indeed. By working late into the night *(bottom)*, all 32 capsules were fitted in just eight days.

"You couldn't help but get caught up in it. I remember I was flying back from Holland on the day the first capsule was lifted into place. The flight landed late in the evening but, even though I had been away the whole week, there was no thought of going home and waiting until morning – I just had to come down to site and see how it had gone. I knew I wouldn't have been able to sleep until I'd seen the pins in place, found out how it had gone, seen what the tolerances were. And it was just such an enormous buzz to see the wheel turning at last, even if there was only the one capsule in place."

Neil Thompson
Design Manager, Mace Limited

It had been realised during the earliest stages of the structural design that the fitting of the capsules to the wheel would be a critical operation. Projected away from the rim, the connection between the capsule and the support frame acts as a cantilever in which the direction of the forces is constantly changing as the wheel rotates. The most efficient connection in these circumstances is a pin-joint, but these must be fitted within very tight tolerances if they are to work properly. With the capsules made in France and the rim in Holland, careful co-ordination had been essential throughout the fabrication process to ensure the two would come together exactly in London. It is a credit to the teamwork that evolved on the project that all went according to plan and the first capsule slotted into place at the first attempt.

"We had carried out extensive tests of the capsule systems all the way through the fabrication phase, of course, in the factory and on the test-rig. The test-rig had been especially useful, letting us run the stability system for extended periods – in fact we were still trying things out there when the real commissioning started on site. But nearly all of those tests had involved only the capsules' internal systems, tested one at a time. Everything changed when we got to site. For the first time we could control and monitor every system on all 32 capsules simultaneously. It was a painstaking operation. Every system had to be tested again individually, partly to ensure they were all fully operational, but also – and more importantly – to ensure they were all feeding back accurate information to the control room on the boarding platform. Everything had to be checked and rechecked."

Steve Saint-Soutane
Installation Supervisor, Semer SA

Connection to the rim's main power supply had been made as each capsule was lifted into place, so it only remained for a few safety checks to be made and the power to be switched on for the final commissioning and testing of the capsules to begin.

"Communication between the control room and capsules is carried out by radio. We had considered running a cable link to each capsule, using a bus-bar system similar to that used to provide power to the rim, but we were concerned that possible breaks in the connection might corrupt the flow of information. That could happen with radio links too, of course, but we have guarded against that by using a spread-spectrum system where several wavebands are monitored simultaneously, allowing the information to be transferred automatically via the strongest signal. These operate at frequencies significantly different from those used by other communication systems, and the transmitters are highly directional, so there is virtually no chance of interference. With so many sensors on each capsule, we are talking about an enormous amount of information. Fortunately, we have installed a number of large networks, so although much of this work was very time-consuming, it was relatively straightforward. We were actually far more interested in the close liaison we needed to establish with other companies. We usually work on our own projects, but here it was necessary to build good working relationships and to find technical solutions that were not only good for ourselves but that linked well with others. In fact, the level of co-operation on site was very good indeed, and the work went very well."

Marc Bottollier
Project Manager, Semer SA

With each capsule incorporating sensors for temperature, lighting, electrical supply, battery back-up, clutch, drive motor, the doors, whether they are open or closed, locked or unlocked, for the escape hatch, the inclinometers, smoke detectors and so on — nearly all of which are duplicated for safety reasons and many which have to interact with other systems — the commissioning, unsurprisingly, was an arduous and time-consuming process that took the best part of three months to complete.

The last capsule was fitted to the rim on Sunday 14 November 1999, and by the end of the month regular test runs of the wheel were able to confirm that the capsule stability systems were operating exactly as planned. In the run up to Christmas and, indeed, through the New Year and well into January — in fact, until all the required safety checks had been approved and signed off — the wheel had to turn with the capsules empty, as seen here *(above)* from one of the restraint towers, the capsule bathed in late afternoon sunshine. Some idea of the view future passengers might enjoy, however, was possible to those with a head for heights and the stamina to climb the 75 or so metres to the small platform suspended immediately below the hub and spindle *(main spread)*.

"I think it is fair to say that the amount of work we undertook between September '98 and December '99 was far greater than any of us had ever envisaged. I was in the fortunate – or maybe unfortunate – position of being able to assess nearly every aspect of the project and, for whatever reason, there is no disguising the fact that it was nowhere near as advanced as we thought it was. All the permissions we needed before work could commence on site, the various issues with the local authorities, the engineering chal-

lenges, the overall complexity of getting all the different pieces to site at the right time – nearly every aspect, when looked at it in detail, was far harder to resolve and far more time-consuming than we had ever thought. Quite frankly, I was amazed, come December '99, that we were still there or there-abouts with the programme. I believe a good many of us will look back on this project as one of the highlights of our professional lives, in part because of the unique challenge it provided, but also because of the intensity

of the whole experience, the intensity of the relationships we established and the intensity of the camaraderie we all enjoyed. Despite the odd glitch, the odd embarrass-ment – of which there were always going to be a few – the construction has been a resounding success. And that, in itself, is a testament to the unreserved dedication and perseverance of the whole team."

Tim Renwick
Project Director, Mace Limited

By late November, when the photographs included here were taken, the wheel may have been up and running, but there was still a considerable amount of work to do. First and foremost, the last of the temporary river platforms, including the one installed to facilitate the lifting of the capsules *(below)*, had to be dismantled so that the large construction barges could be withdrawn. Only then could work begin on the fitting of the ferry pier and collision protection system. One of the contractors under greatest pressure during this period was T. Clarke plc, the company responsible for the installation of the project's electrical supply network. Their key priority had been to provide a permanent supply as quickly as possible, first to the main drive system — so that the wheel could be turned as the capsules were fitted — and then to the rim itself — so that commissioning of the capsules could commence. This was no easy task, not least because work on site prior to the uplift had prevented the installation of the main supply cables from the project's own 11,000 volt underground substation, next to Belvedere Road, out to the distribution switchrooms on the boarding platform. Access to the switchrooms was also extremely limited, but by working through the night, an intermittent supply was available by the end of October, with full power following a few weeks later.

"But here we are, we've done it. We have allowed a huge edifice to be erected in the middle of one of our proudest heritage sites. We've put up the most unlikely, improbable and quite useless construction London has ever seen and it's magnificent. One cannot help but smile as one looks at it. It lifts the heart and fires the imagination."

Stewart Steven
The Mail on Sunday, 12 December 1999

To minimise wind-induced vibrations, the main backstays are interconnected at key points over their length *(above left)* and fitted with 'shock absorbers' at their base *(left)*.

Planning guidelines have limited the number of on-site installations to two timber-faced kiosks, delivered to site in prefabricated sections *(above)*, one a snackbar and coffee outlet, and the other a small shop.

"Though I have shared an office with David and Julia since well before the original competiton, my first serious involvement in the project only came during the run-up to the planning application in April 1996, when David asked me to outline some initial ideas. The design of the wheel had developed enormously by that time and, following discussions with the owners, there was now a clearly defined site, extending exactly 30-metres from the North Retaining Wall that separates the sunken access road running

Unfortunately, the delayed uplift was to have a serious impact on the completion of the landscaping. Aware that much of the site would now be required for access and storage well into the New Year, priority was given only to the pedestrian bridge linking the site to a new side entrance to County Hall *(below)* and to those areas immediately around the boarding platform and the kiosks. The rest of the site would have to be completed at a later date. Following the installation of the underground services in mid-November, work began immediately with the laying of the granite sets and the fabrication of the reinforced concrete bench that forms the boundary between the site and Jubilee Gardens.

along the side of County Hall from the rest of Jubilee Gardens. I realised that there was little point in competing with the wheel, as it already had a strong identity of its own. Instead, I proposed a fairly neutral space — consciously without style, if you will — based on good quality natural materials used in a fairly straightforward way. The main structure of the design, then as now, was provided by an avenue of trees — running the length of the site on axis with the wheel — that creates a formal approach for those arriving from that direction, while at the same time defining more relaxed areas on either side, suitable for a wide range of activities. My main concern, always, was that as much of the site as possible should be seen as a new public urban space, open to all. From that point on, there have only been two significant changes: the first concerning the boundary with Jubilee Gardens, which I had left deliberately ambiguous in the first design to allow for future developments on that part of the site; the second to do with a request for increased security, particularly in terms of vehicular access to the site. With no way of predicting what was likely to happen to Jubilee Gardens at that stage, the Planning Officer suggested we treat our site as an isolated design. Quite frankly, I was a little surprised, but in security terms it worked out well, allowing the installation of the continuous 'bench' along that side of the site."

Edward Hutchison
Landscape Architect

By the week before Christmas, preparations for the official switching on of the wheel on New Year's Eve were well advanced. The ferry pier and its access bridges were now in place and the permanent lighting for the whole site was up and running. With a stately rim speed of just 0.26 metres per second — or a little over half a mile per hour — when the wheel is turning at its normal operating speed, movement of the capsules is almost indiscernible during the day, and only shows up on the night view from the Royal Horseguards Hotel, on the far side of the river (below), because of the photograph's 15-second exposure. The sunset view (left) from the roof of the nearby Shell Building's north wing, on the other hand, was taken when the wheel was stationery, allowing the rim to stand out in sharp silhouette against the western sky.

One of the main reasons for assembling the wheel horizontally had been to avoid the increased difficulties — and dangers — incurred by working at height should it have been built vertically. Following the uplift, of course, some work at height and in exposed locations, was unavoidable — not least during the removal of the cast-steel 'hood' that had held the temporary support cables at the back of the spindle *(opposite page, bottom)*. Specially trained in all forms of climbing, abseiling and working from ropes, much of this work — including the installation of the support sleeves *(far right)* that protect the spoke cables against undue bending at their connection to the rim — was undertaken by operatives from CAN Limited.

"The curious thing is that the extreme pressure of building such a high-profile project helped make it a success. Because everydody knew this was a special opportunity, like building a new Eiffel Tower, they were willing to find the extra time and make sure they gave the best advice. The best people wanted to be involved and they too were willing to give that extra 10 per cent. This is reflected in the accuracy of the rim Privately, we had assumed that the best construction tolerances we could hope for, in terms of the rim being out of plane, would probably be around ±100mm — although we had actually allowed for more than twice that amount. In fact, the final survey has confirmed that no point on the rim is out of alignment by more than 40mm. To put that in context, if the wheel was scaled down to the size of a bicycle wheel, the rim would be out of true by less than one-third of a millimetre."

Professor Jacques Berenbak
Senior Design Engineer, Hollandia BV

With the wheel turning, regular inspections are now carried out in the space between the hub and spindle *(right)*, that gives access to the main bearings, and inside the spindle itself *(far right)*.

"For all the overt commercialism of the wheel, there's something disconcerting, even radical, about being able to look down on the Houses of Parliament and Whitehall. This is a part of London that makes its citizens feel like outsiders, dwarfed by huge ministry buildings and equestrian statues. But from the wheel, Whitehall will now look rather small"

Jonathan Jones
The Guardian, 30 August 1999

Final fit-out of the ferry pier pontoon was carried out at Tilbury Docks *(far left and below)*, while the floating booms *(left)* were fabricated at Tilbury Douglas's own works at Belevedere.

"Considering all the difficulties of the site – the limited access, working over water, too many people in too small a space – it is all the more impressive that we avoided any serious injuries. And, as far as I know, noboby fell in the river. Actually, that's not quite true. One person did slip and half fall in, but he was pulled out quickly so I don't think that counts."

Jan Stam
Site Operations Manager, Hollandia BV

Conceived by The Beckett Rankine Partnership and developed through to detail design by Tony Gee & Partners, with specialist support from Houlder Offshore Engineering, the independent ferry pier is actually part of the wheel's collision protection system. The pier itself — actually a floating pontoon — its access bridges and the floating booms, that stretch at an angle from both ends of the pier to the river wall, act as a unified system, capable of halting a 2200-tonne vessel travelling at 8 knots — this being the largest vessel that uses the Thames on a regular basis. With time at a premium, Tilbury Douglas subcontracted the fabrication of the pontoon to Wear Engineering, while the access bridges were built by their sister company Nusteel and fitted out by Littlehampton Engineering.

"Our first involvement with the project came about when a couple of boat operators we regularly work with mentioned they thought there should be a ferry pier associated with it. From the drawings we had seen — this was around October '97 — we knew there was a fairly straightforward boom arrangement that acted as a collision protection system, but there was no provision for landing boats. Working speculatively, we came up with a scheme which replaced that design with a floating pontoon, held out in the river by a pair of access bridges (or brows) that act as radial arms, with the collision protection booms now held at each end. By connecting the booms to a series of energy absorbing units manufactured by Jarret of France — similar to hydraulic pistons but filled with silicon putty instead of oil — we calculated there should be enough elastic deformation in the system to stop even the largest boats. Of course, this would be more expensive, but it should have been possible to recoup the costs from the boat operators. As it turned out, when Marks Barfield Architects asked us to develop the concept, we found out that the Millennium Commission was willing to fund half the cost themselves as part of their programme to promote transport on the river. In the end, of course, we became involved in the project in another capacity and the scheme was worked up by others, but it is still nice to know we played our part.

Tim Beckett
Partner, The Beckkett Rankine Partnership

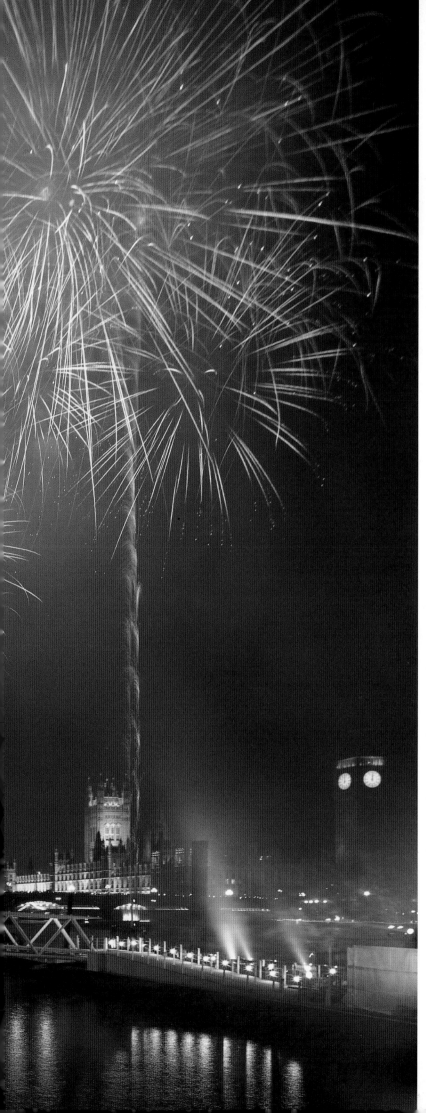

Midnight on New Year's Eve, and the 'River of Fire' explodes over the British Airways London Eye to welcome in the new millennium. It had been accepted some months before that any chance of opening to the public on 1 January 2000 was just not on — it had always been asking a great deal to expect that what had initially been conceived as a two-year construction programme could be completed in just 15 months. Even so, it had seemed that sufficient capsules would be ready to allow a limited number of private guests to enjoy a ride on this special night. And all seemed to be going well until, quite unexpectedly on the day before New Year's Eve, a fault was detected in the clutch on one of the capsule stability systems. An identical clutch had been running perfectly on Sigma's test-rig in France for more than eight months, but with no time to strip the clutch down and check what the problem might be, there was no alternative but to run the wheel without passengers. It was a bitter disappointment, but everyone agreed that safety was paramount. Subsequent analysis found it to be a rogue manufacturing fault that affected only a handful of clutches, but as an extra precaution all have since been replaced.

From the beginning of January, while the final fit-out of the boarding platform continued *(right and below left)* key personnel from British Airways London Eye's own technical and operating staff — who had already undertaken extensive training off-site — started the lengthy procedure of acclimatising themselves to the working conditions on the wheel itself, under the watchful eye of Operations Manager Paul Kelly and Technical Operations Manager Kevin Dyer *(below right, top and centre).*

I have been involved with the project since July '99, liaising with the manufacturers to gain a complete understanding of all the systems, then deciding what size team was required and arranging their training. We have ended up with 17 engineers in all — all with backgrounds in fields where public safety is a priority — who work round the clock in shifts, with three on duty during the day and five on call for overnight maintenance and testing. This is a lot heavier than usual, mainly because the critical parts tend to be those that carry passengers. On a normal ride that usually means no more than one or two trains, but here, of course, there are 32 capsules, each of which has to be checked individually. Every morning, before the wheel opens to the public, each aspect of the wheel that is safety critical or will affect passenger comfort is checked, either visually or more often via the computer, while some — the door locks, for example — are tested manually. It is a time-consuming operation that can take the night crew anything up to *four hours to complete, over and above any other work that might have been necessary. And, of course, many of the systems are unique, so we couldn't be entirely sure how they would perform in practice. More than a few have required constant monitoring and only now, after five months of running, are we settling into a steady routine."*

Kevin Dyer
Technical Operations Manager,
British Airways London Eye

"There is so much information coming back from each capsule that we decided early on that all of the systems would have to be self-monitoring to one degree or another. In normal operations, there are two displays available to the operator: one showing the whole wheel and indicating the position and operational status of each capsule; and a second that focuses on each capsule in turn, showing both the key information — temperature, attitude and so on — and which systems are running. If a fault is located, the appropriate display shows up immediately on the monitor, the part in question flagged by colour. If the fault is minor, the computer will offer the operator a choice of options; if serious, it will initiate the appropriate action automatically, stopping the wheel completely if necessary. Further layers of information can then be accessed by the technical staff, who will decide on the next course of action".

Marc Bottollier
Project Manager, Semer SA

253

In its final form, the site landscaping can be identified as two separate zones: with hard-wearing granite sets at the top of the site, laid out to a strict grid around the two kiosks and towards the boarding platform, where visitors will naturally congregate; and the more relaxed approach, dominated by the avenue of semi-mature double-white flowering cherry trees *(opposite)* and open areas of Cotswold gravel separated by granite steps *(below)*. A bed of ground-cover bamboo and evergreen grasses protects the North Retaining Wall — a listed structure — and complements the 10-metre high trees. Some 15 years old, the trees could well grow to a height of 60 metres over the next 50 years. Creating a *cordon sanitaire* around the wheel, the security features have been cleverly disguised as public seating: the wall separating the site from Jubilee Gardens as a granite-faced bench topped by a hedge, and the individual bollards as solid granite seats, measuring 400mm square and standing 600mm high.

"Not so long ago it seemed to we sceptics (for I had company) that the wheel was a clown's nose on the face of the city, a funfair ride that would suffuse the skyline with the smell of hot dogs and popcorn, and blast its oompah music over the grave concert and public buildings in Parliament Square and Whitehall. And as the first Ferris Wheel was built in the last century, the wheel seemed like a curiously old-fashioned way of celebrating the next one. . . But the point the sceptics missed was that the sheer energy of the thing, and the simple joys it offers, outweigh the negatives. And we need not have worried so much about the wheel's threat to the dignity of Parliament, as the architecture of Barry and Pugin is not such a fragile flower as to be overwhelmed by a big circle of white-painted steel."

Rowan Moore
The Evening Standard, 18 October 1999

The Tussaud's Group, the partner on the client team responsible for the day-to-day running of the wheel, had hoped that opening in February would allow a couple of relatively quiet months during which the operating staff could settle into their jobs and establish the necessary routines to keep the wheel running smoothly at all times. A few busy weekends were to be expected during the first weeks, but these would be outweighed by quieter weekdays. Advanced ticket sales, however, indicated that the wheel could well run at capacity every day. With the commissioning of the capsules delayed slightly by the need to replace all the clutch units, the decision was therefore made to open at the beginning of February as planned, but with limited ticket sales for the first month.

"We spent a great deal of time refining the organisational systems we would need to control boarding and disembarkation from the wheel. There were the physical requirements — the length and width of the ramps, for example — but there were also other issues more to do with queue management — such as segregating 25 people per capsule while keeping groups of friends and family together. Of course, some of this is familiar to us from our other attractions, but a number of proposals — including fixed boarding times — were not. With forecasts indicating we could be running at capacity from day one, it only made sense that we try and sort out as many of these issues in advance as possible and, to this end, we actually built a boarding platform out of wood, down at Chessington, and asked our staff to come in early over several mornings so that we could try out different options.

Andrew Potter
General Manager, The Tussaud's Group

"With up to 800 people on the wheel at any one time, there are a great many safety issues to be addressed. Taking the capsules as an example, we have had to consider what happens if any of a number of mechanical systems fail. How can we ensure the doors can never be opened by mistake? What happens if wheel gets stuck? Worse still, what happens if a capsule turns over? Every possibility, however minor, had to be looked at in detail and the appropriate safety measure implemented. Even then, for this to be done effectively, it was not enough to know what might go wrong, you had to understand how it goes wrong and why. A logical progression had to be established, which extended to considering the effects of those systems introduced to stop other things going wrong — what happens if the back-up fails? It was an endless line of 'what if' questions, each of which had to be answered with care."

Allan Mann
Technical Director, Babtie Allott & Lomax

The official opening of British Airways London Eye was held on a rather grey Thursday morning, on 9 March 2000, in the presence of over 1000 assembled guests and team members — with the rest of the day given over to rides for the press and the media. The wheel had already proved very popular during February, but the crowds that flocked to London's newest attraction over that first weekend after the opening *(below)* took everyone by surprise. Inevitably, there have been a few teething troubles — air movement through the capsules proved too slow during the first few months, causing them to overheat on the sunniest days and allowing condensation to form on the wettest — but the correct procedures have since been implemented and further improvements will be introduced in the coming months.

If the fine-tuning of the capsules has taken a little longer than planned, the main drive and stability systems on the restraint tower *(opposite)* have run almost perfectly from day one. The effortless ability of the hydraulic drive system to stop and start the wheel so smoothly has proved a particular revelation. During normal operations, the capsules can be brought to a complete stop in just two metres with no discernible movement of any kind. Indeed, the deceleration profile for the hydraulics has been refined so precisely that emergency stops within half a metre can be effected with absolute safety. As with nearly all the systems on the wheel, there are two entirely independent electrical supplies, both to the drive system and to the rim *(below right)*, controlled through the two main switchrooms on the boarding platform, each of which is capable of supplying all the main systems independently. A back-up generator, situated in the substation, cuts in automatically in the event of a power cut, with sufficient power to operate all essential services.

"There was a lot of discussion in the early days about whether the capsules should be air-conditioned at all, and we did look at the options, but it quickly became clear that the capsules had to be enclosed — and that being the case, there was little alternative. With that decision made, what was imperative was to keep the energy demands as low as possible by specifying the most efficient systems wherever we could. With a power input of around 12 kilowatts each, one can't escape the fact that the capsules are intensively serviced, but this has to balanced against the fact that this benefits up to 25 people. An office of similar floor area might require a third of the power input, but would benefit no more than two or three. The reality is that a small family will probably expend more energy driving the few miles to their local station than they will use on the wheel."

Loren Butt
Managing Director, Loren Butt Consultancies

With 32 capsules, each capable of carrying 25 passengers, the wheel has a maximum capacity of 1600 people per hour, though in practice ticket sales are normally limited to around 1400 to allow for the inevitable delays that occur in operations of this complexity. Open between 10am and 6pm during the winter months — from October to March — and from 9am to 10pm during the summer, target estimates had initially assumed peak capacities of around 14,000 people per day during the busiest periods, with markedly quieter days in between. In reality, the quieter days have been few and far between — even the rain, it seems, has done little to dampen enthusiasm — and over the first six months of operation the wheel has been averaging 11,000 per day. Indeed, on more than one occasion, daily through-put has reached 17,000 — exceeding the predicted 100 per cent occupancy rate by a considerable margin.

"Looking back at it now, it was all the ups and downs, the stresses and strains, the failures and successes, that actually made this such a special experience. I don't think it would have had the same emotional appeal had it all gone like clockwork. And though I didn't feel like it at the time, there is part of me that wouldn't have had it any other way."

Paul Baxter
Project Director, British Airways

"Originally, we were planning for a permanent staff of around 75, with extra help brought in seasonally as required. Based on our experience with other attractions, you can normally predict when the busiest times will be – summer weekends, bank holidays, Easter and so on – and plan accordingly. But here, we have been running at capacity from the very beginning, with no 'down' time at all. I can't deny that this has caused a whole raft of problems, and it has made for a very chaotic few months. Of course, it is better to be managing success rather than failure, but it has not been ideal and I am only grateful that most of our visitors have been so patient. Thankfully, the systems are now falling into place and we have taken on the staff and management personnel – a full-time staff of 225, split into three shifts – to keep things running smoothly, even on the busiest of days. It has been a very steep learning curve but, quite frankly, I would not have missed it for the world. I am a lot older, I'm a lot greyer, but to be part of a project loved by all has been a fabulous experience. Everyone, it seems, wants to have a go. Age is not a barrier. Social class is not a barrier. It really is open to all. One only has to see the list of celebrities, politicians, ambassadors and even royalty who have visited in the past few months to realise what an extraordinary impact the wheel has had."

Paul Kelly
Operations Manager, British Airways London Eye

263

By April 2000, just one month after the wheel's official opening and a mere six months since its uplift in the previous October, the gentle curve of British Airways London Eye arching across the skyline of the city had already become a familiar landmark, visible from all over central London — including St James's Park *(left)* — and beyond. From closer vantage points, in particular from the Embankment on the far side of the river, the true scale and grandeur of the wheel is immediately apparent, as in this view *(main spread)* taken at dawn, with the top-most capsules and the towers of the Houses of Parliament glinting in the first of the day's sunshine.

As Henry Mayhew noted after an ascent in a hot-air balloon as long ago as 1882 *(see page 20)*, "there is an innate desire in all men to view the earth and its cities from exceeding high places", a fact confirmed by the immense popularity enjoyed by British Airways London Eye since it first opened. On fair days, and even foul, the world's tallest observation wheel offers unrivalled and ever changing views. Indeed, one of its major successes has been the number of times visitors have returned to enjoy London's many different aspects. On a clear day, the view can be breathtaking but, as shown here, even the dreariest can be transformed at dusk, with the lights of the city picking out landmarks not always visible during the day.

"I have been reading, recently, about the problems Gustave Eiffel encountered during the construction of his famous tower. There are so many parallels. I was particularly taken by his comment that, for him, the tower was a symbol for all the challenges that had been overcome. There is a wonderful double edge to that. Building a project like this isn't just about the tecnology or the engineering – as Julia and I have found to our cost. On the one hand, there have been so many highs and lows to plough through over the past six years – to find the right partners, to convince the planners, to lock-in the funding and so on, a constant roller coaster – that you can't help but be reminded of that. But then there are other moments, often when we catch sight of the wheel unexpectedly, when it sparkles and looks so good, that we can only marvel at what we have achieved."

David Marks
Director, Marks Barfield Architects

The wheel from Waterloo Bridge, reflected almost perfectly in the still water of a slack tide early on a bright summer's morning. At the time of writing in August 2000, a little over six months after opening to the public, British Airways London Eye has already entertained more than two million visitors, marking it as one of the most successful visitor attractions in Europe.

It is somewhat humbling to realise that the majority of the construction photographs illustrating this book were taken within a 12 month period – between March 1999 and February 2000. The work that was achieved in that time, in its range, its scale and complexity, is truly remarkable and it has been a privilege to share, if only in part, in the commitment and enthusiasm of those involved in the successful completion of this extraordinary project.

A great many people helped me along the way during this time, either by sorting out the practical issues of access and travel – and so ensuring I was, more often than not, in the right place at the right time – or, and more importantly, by finding the time in their busy schedules to talk to me and explain what was going on. There are far too many to name here, but to one and all I extend my sincere thanks. I can only hope I have captured something of your passion and integrity in this book.

On a more practical note, for all their help during the design and production of this book I would also like to extend my thanks to the following: Frank Anatole, Annie Booth, Julia Barfield, Jane Capper and Chris Cowpe, Lesley Chisholm, Sandra Colosimo, Andrea Conti, Roberto Conti, Fiona Hanan, Christianne and Robert Long, David Marks, William McElhinney, Arianne Roedolfs, Prue Saunders, Lavinia Stoneham Renzo Toti and his team in the pre-press department at Conti Tipocolor, and Nick Wood for his generous assistance with much of the photography.

Please note that the photographs taken by Ian Lambot now form part of a permanent archive to be held and supervised by the British Airways London Eye Company.

Ian Lambot, August 2000

Rather than identify each picture individually, the figure in brackets below indicates only the total number of images attributed to each contributor on a specific page or spread, where that number is more than one.

Nic Bailey   202/203(1) 203(2)
Richard Bryant / Arcaid   15
The Booth Family Collection   8 9 13 133(1)
FAG Kugelfischer Georg Schäfer AG   86(1) 87(1) 88/89 89(2)
Hulton Getty Picture Collection   11 12 16/17(2) 17
Marks Barfield Architects   18 21 22(2) 26(4) 26/27 30 31 32/33 102(3) 203(1)
Iv-Infra   66(1) 67
Ian Lambot   33(2) 34 36(2) 38(3) 39(2) 40(2) 40/41 41(2) 42(4) 43(7) 44(4) 44/45 50(5) 51(5) 52(2) 52/53 54(4) 55(3) 56 56/57 58 59(3) 60(2) 60/61(1) 62(2) 62/63 64 65 66(1) 68(4) 72(1) 72/73 74 75(1) 76(3) 77(3) 78(3) 79(2) 80 80/81 82(2) 82/83 83(2) 84(2) 84/85 86(3) 87(6) 90(3) 90/91 92(7) 93(5) 96 96/97 97(2) 98/99 99 100 106(3) 107(2) 108(3) 109(6) 112(2) 113(4) 114 114/115 118(1) 118/119 120(6) 121(4) 122(2) 124(5) 125(3) 126/127 128(3) 130(2) 130/131 131 132/133 133(1) 134(2) 134/135 135 140/141 141(2) 142(5) 143(3) 144/145(2) 145(3) 146(3) 147(6) 148(3) 149(4) 150(3) 150/151 152 153 154(6) 155(5) 156 156/157 157(2) 158(5) 159(5) 160(4) 162(7) 163(4) 168(1) 169(1) 170/171(1) 171(2) 172(4) 173(7) 174(2) 174/175 176(3) 177(5) 178(1) 178/179(2) 180/181 182/183 184(2) 184/185 185(2) 186(3) 187(6) 188/189(2) 189(3) 190(4) 191(7) 192/193 193 194(4) 195(3) 199 200 202/203(1) 204(1) 205(2) 206/207(2) 208(4) 209(3) 210 210/211 212(6) 213(4) 214/215(2) 215 216(5) 217(4) 219(3) 220(5) 221(1) 222 224(6) 225(4) 228/229 229(2) 230(3) 231(5) 232(5) 233(5) 237 239 240/241(2) 241(3) 242(7) 243(4) 244/245 245 246(4) 247(4) 248(1) 249(4) 250/251 252(4) 253(7) 254 255(4) 256(2) 256/257(1) 258/259 259 260(3) 261 262(3) 262/263(1) 267 270
William McElhinney   36/37 66/67
Museum of London   20/21
Collection of The New-York Historical Society   14 neg no: 73799
Nick Wood   Cover 2/3 28/29 29 33(1) 35 36(1) 38(2) 39(4) 46/47/48 49 60(1) 60/61(1) 68(1) 69 70 70/71 71 72(1) 75(1) 76(2) 77(2) 78(1) 90(1) 94(2) 95 101 102/103 104(2) 104/105 105 107(2) 108(1) 109(1) 110/111 111 112(1) 113(2) 116 117 118(2) 120(1) 122/123 125(2) 127(2) 128(1) 129 136/137/138 139 143(1) 155(1) 161 164/165/166 167 168(5) 169(4) 170/171(1) 171(1) 177(1) 178(1) 180(2) 181 183(2) 194(1) 196/197/198 201 204(6) 205(2) 206(3) 218/219 220(1) 220/221 221(1) 222/223 223 224(1) 226(3) 226/227(2) 230(1) 234/235/236 238 248(3) 251 256(1) 256/257(1) 262/263(1) 264/265/266 268 269
Nick Wood / Marks Barfield Architects   19 23 24/25(2)

Credits